A LIVING FROM THE

Devon's Fishing Industry and its Fishermen

Compiled and Edited by M.G. Dickinson

DEVON BOOKS

First published in Great Britain in 1987 by Devon Books

Copyright © M. G. Dickinson

ISBN: 0 86114-803-7

All rights reserved. No part of this publication may be reproduced, stored in a retrieval system, or transmitted in any form or by any means, electronic, mechanical, photocopying, recording or otherwise, without the prior permission of the copyright holder.

British Library Cataloguing in Publication Data

A Living from the sea: Devon's fishing industry and its fishermen.
1. Fisheries—England—Devon—History
I. Dickinson, M.G. 338.3'727'094235 SH258.D4/

Typeset by Plymouth Reprographic Company Ltd.
Printed and bound in Great Britain by A. Wheaton & Co. Ltd

DEVON BOOKS
Official Publisher to Devon County Council

An imprint of Wheaton Publishers Ltd, a member of Pergamon/BPCC Publishing Corporation PLC

Wheaton Publishers Ltd
Hennock Road, Marsh Barton, Exeter, Devon EX2 8RP
Tel: 0392 74121; Telex: 42794 (WHEATN G)

SALES
Direct sales enquiries to Devon Books at the address above.

Trade sales to: Town & Country Books, P.O. Box 31, Newton Abbot, Devon TQ12 5AQ
Tel: 080 47 2690

Front Cover illustration: 'View of the Ness; entrance to Teignmouth Harbour'. Thomas Luny, 1809 (Teignmouth Town Council and Royal Albert Memorial Museum, Exeter)

Back cover illustration: 'A Fisherman's Cottage'. Thomas Luny, 1817 (Royal Albert Memorial Museum, Exeter)

Title page illustration:
Blackheaded Gull in winter plumage, painted by F.W.L Ross of Topsham, 1874 (West Country Studies Library)

CONTENTS

Left:
Tongue-in-cheek representation by Peter Orlando Hutchinson of the fisherfolk at
Beer bringing a dead whale ashore on 1 February 1876. The picture is
nevertheless a unique pictorial record of fishermen and women and of their craft
(West Country Studies Library)

Above:
'Fresh Breeze at Sidmouth'. Undated watercolour by Peter Orlando Hutchinson.
A fisherman struggles with the lugsail whilst his companion grips the tiller (West
Country Studies Library)

ACKNOWLEDGEMENTS

This compilation began as a co-operative venture between the Exeter and Plymouth branches of the Devon Record Office. It consists of papers already in print but scattered through a variety of different journals, linking passages containing original research, and reproduction of paintings, prints and documents.

The editorship is that of Michael Dickinson, upon whom rests all responsibility for such shortcomings and inaccuracies as the book may contain. The help of all colleagues at the Devon Record Office is gratefully acknowledged, but especially that of Richard Burley at the West Devon Record Office. Much of his original research material has been assimilated into the text and the location of suitable sources for Plymouth in particular and West Devon in general is due to him. To Colin McDonald are due thanks for running to earth the painting of packing fish on the Barbican, Plymouth.

An anthology is almost wholly dependent on the goodwill of those whose flowers the editor has picked and most grateful thanks are due to the authors and editors of journals whose response has been unfailingly kind and positive.

Efforts to contact Michael Straight, author of the valuable and hitherto unpublished *Report on the Brixham Fishing Industry*, through publishers in London and in New York have proved of no avail. The most grateful acknowledgement and fullest apology are made for any loss to him or to those unknown to the editor through the use of this source.

The following people, publishers and the editors of the respective journals concerned have released copyright to the present editor and publisher.

Crispin Gill and the Sutton Harbour Improvement Company for *Fishing from Sutton Harbour*.

Professor Melvin Firestone, the Editor of *Folk Life*, and the Editor of *Stokenham Occasional Papers* for *The Technology of the Traditional Start Bay Crab Fishery*.

Dorothy Dix and the Editor of the *Transactions of the Devonshire Association* for *Lobster and Crab Pots in the South Hams*.

The Executive Editor of the Marine Biological Association of the United Kingdom for *The Brixham Fishing Grounds and Fishery Statistics*.

John Horsley and the Torbay Borough Council for *The Trawl Net*.

Conrad Dixon and the Editor of *Mariner's Mirror* for *The Exeter Whale Fishery Company*.

Dr Jeffery Porter and the Editor of *Devon and Cornwall Notes and Queries* for *The Teign Oyster Beds*.

The late Canon John Andrews and the Editor of *Devon and Cornwall Notes and Queries* for *Umberleigh Weir*

Dr Neville Oswald and the Editor of the *Transactions of the Devonshire Association* for *Devon and the Cod Fishery of Newfoundland*

Thanks are likewise due to owners of original documents from which texts have been taken: J.F.G. Michelmore, the Exeter Diocesan Registrar; Mr R.A. Waller of Clinton Devon Estates; Lord Courtenay; Mrs Morris of Gloucester; and the Revd D.A. Bates of Clovelly.

FOREWORD

Michael Dickinson's study of aspects of the development of Devon's fishing industry is both interesting and valuable. Despite the importance of fishing in the life of the coastal communities of the county relatively little has been published about its history. The present work is full of information which will be new to many readers. Take, for instance, the fact that a toll on pilchards landed in Devon and Cornwall made a significant contribution to the cost of the fort built more or less on the site of the Plymouth Citadel between 1592 and 1595 – and the result was a falling off in landings at Plymouth, where the toll was collected, and a rise in landings at Cornish ports, where the toll was less rigorously enforced. Or take the researches of Professor Melvin Firestone of Arizona State University who, unlikely as it may seem, studied the fishing community at Hallsands in 1974 and 1975. Professor Firestone's work is in the best traditions of American scholarship in this field and can be compared with the excellent work which has been done in recent years in the study of Newfoundland fishing communities.

Running through this book, as it must through any study of a maritime aspect of the history of Devon, is the Newfoundland connection. Few people realise today how vitally important a part codfish, caught off the coast of Newfoundland and dried and salted to preserve it for long periods, played in the development of Europe in earlier centuries. It is true to say that armies marched on it, long voyages to explore and develop trade were made on it, and industrial and agricultural communities subsisted on it. The product, salt fish, is still obtainable today in some delicatessen shops and what was once a staple food of the poor is now something of a luxury.

In the trade, first of catching the cod, salting and then carrying it to Europe, later of carrying it from Newfoundland and Labrador Outports to Britain and the Continent, Devon played a vital role for as long as the business lasted in its traditional forms. The editor makes this very clear in his selections. He does not, however, perhaps make it quite clear how long the trade lasted. It underwent a revival for reasons connected with the structure of the business in Newfoundland at the end of the last century and the very last British sailing vessel to be employed in this historic business, which reaches back before Cabot's voyages and played its part in the early British settlement of North America, was a Devon schooner, the *Lady St Johns* built at Kingsbridge and registered at Salcombe, and she made her last passage from Newfoundland as late as 1930.

Basil Greenhill
Exeter University

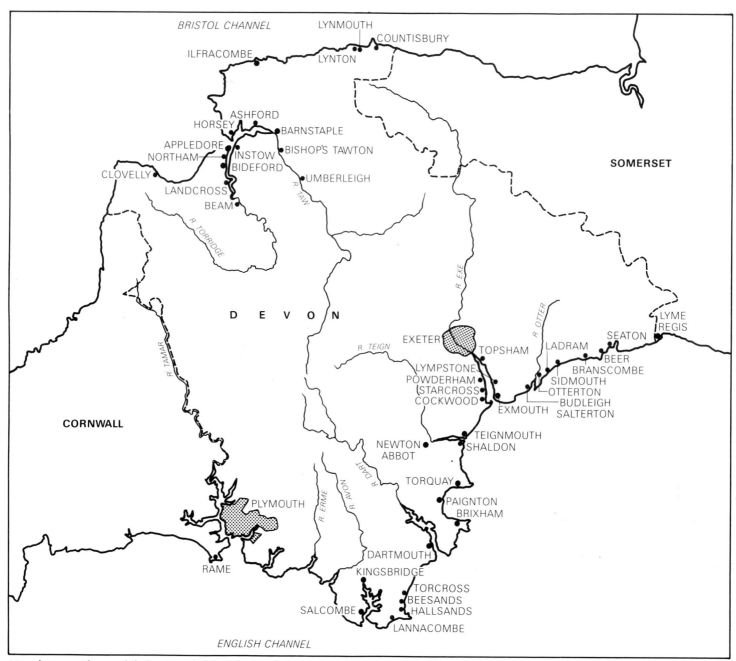

BRISTOL CHANNEL

LYNMOUTH
COUNTISBURY
ILFRACOMBE
LYNTON

ASHFORD
HORSEY
BARNSTAPLE
APPLEDORE
BISHOP'S TAWTON
NORTHAM
INSTOW
BIDEFORD
CLOVELLY
UMBERLEIGH
LANDCROSS
BEAM

SOMERSET

R. TAW

R. TORRIDGE

D E V O N

R. EXE

R. TAMAR

R. OTTER

LYME
REGIS
SEATON
EXETER
R. TEIGN
TOPSHAM
LADRAM
BEER
BRANSCOMBE
LYMPSTONE
POWDERHAM
SIDMOUTH
STARCROSS
OTTERTON
COCKWOOD
BUDLEIGH
EXMOUTH
SALTERTON

CORNWALL

TEIGNMOUTH
NEWTON
SHALDON
ABBOT

TORQUAY

R. ERME
R. AVON
R. DART

PAIGNTON
PLYMOUTH
BRIXHAM

RAME

DARTMOUTH
KINGSBRIDGE
TORCROSS
BEESANDS
SALCOMBE
HALLSANDS
LANNACOMBE

ENGLISH CHANNEL

Map of Devon with some of the locations which have been involved in Devon's
fishing industry since its earliest times

INTRODUCTION

Since the 1950s over-fishing and consequent political pressures have turned the pattern of the European fishing industry upside down. For Devon it is a pleasant irony that these changes have led to the re-emergence of Plymouth and Brixham as fishing centres. The scale of over-fishing may be unprecedented, but it is possibly worth recalling that changing shoal patterns and even 'cod wars' have not been confined to the twentieth century.

This is a compilation of published and unpublished articles on the history of the fishing industry in Devon's rivers, around Devon's coasts and by Devonians in far-off waters. To these have been added linking passages, some involving original research, together with extracts from original source material to be found in the Devon Record Office.

Prey ranging in size from oysters to whales has been included, fished for in environments ranging from the River Taw to the Grand Banks of Newfoundland, at dates between the Middle Ages and the present century.

The earliest documentation on Devon fisheries concerns its rivers. As Professor Hoskins relates, in the Saxon and Medieval period these teemed with fish as the rivers of British Columbia do now. The infamous weir of Countess Isabella de Fortibus was in fact a salmon trap built across the River Exe. (Examples of the information to be found among Medieval and Tudor sources is given in the section on the fisheries of North Devon.)

Among the earliest records of sea fishing is that of the licensing of nets along the South Devon coast in 1566. Eighty-one seine nets and twenty tuck nets are recorded between Axmouth and Plymouth. The greatest concentrations of nets were between Dawlish and Salcombe.

In 1599, Devon and Cornwall were bringing political pressure to bear against the granting of the monopoly of salting fish to one Henry Warner.

However, the West Country turned its attention increasingly towards Newfoundland. By the time of Charles I considerable rights in this trade had been won from competitors in London and on the continent of Europe. The scale of the West Country undertaking becomes all the more impressive when it is remembered that at this time the Dutch were fishing the North Sea well into English 'home' waters. A royal fleet was even sent out against them in 1635.

The following work takes up the story between the seventeenth and twentieth centuries, although only in the cases of Plymouth and Brixham is this extended beyond the Second World War.

The Barbican and Sutton Pool, Plymouth, 1833

— 1 —
PLYMOUTH'S SUTTON POOL

Plymouth's importance as a fishing centre is, perhaps, overshadowed by other aspects of the maritime history of the place which has been the largest urban community in the South West for almost 250 years. Did fishing provide the earliest impetus to raise the rural community at Sutton above subsistence level? The dedication of the parish church to St Andrew – a rare one in the South West – provides the first clue. More than thirty years ago Robert Pearce's articles in the Western Morning News pointed out that the acquisition by the Valletort family of one of the three Sutton manors in 1105 could have brought the transfer of valuable fishing rights to it. Plymouth historian Crispin Gill points out that the existence of experienced pilots could have been one of the factors which brought Edward I's war fleets here during the last quarter of the thirteenth century.

Yet it is only a hundred years later that we have irrefutable proof of a fishing industry. A charter of Richard II in 1378 provides conclusive evidence of the taking of pilchards and hake, and slightly later we may find the first names of individual fisherman – John Goore and Thomas 'Fyschaer'.

With the passing of a further two hundred years we find that Plymouth's commitment to the Newfoundland and New England fisheries was both early, and in comparative terms, massive. (Of this more will be said in chapter 7.)

Another clue as to Plymouth's stake in the fishing industry is the importance formerly given to the 'Fishing Feast'. As with so many Plymouth institutions, this appears to have been already firmly established at the time of its first surviving documentation. Accounts for the year 1730–31 show that £16.12s.6d. was expended – enough for quite a respectable banquet at that date.

The following account of Plymouth's fishing was written expressly for the Sutton Harbour Company by Crispin Gill.

Fishing from Sutton Harbour

When the first Plymouth man had tilled his farm he went fishing. When he had more fish than his family could eat, he was in business. To keep fish it had to be salted, and salt could be obtained in such quantities only from the Biscay shores of France. Here the sun was warm enough to evaporate sea water from shallow pans on the beach, leaving the salt. The French had wine as well as salt to sell, and were happy to buy salt fish. Sutton Harbour was in this trade long before Edward I came down with his soldiers; indeed the King came only because Sutton men and their ships were veterans of the passage round Ushant.

Plymouth has its own rich fishing ground just inside the Eddystone, where hake is the speciality. In Medieval times all hake brought into Sutton Harbour paid a special due to maintain the old four-towered castle – 'castle hake' they were called. When Drake's Fort was being built the Crown tried to pay for it by means of a special levy on all pilchards exported from Devon and Cornwall, but it was a hard struggle to collect the money. In any case Sutton Harbour's pilchard trade was being stolen from 1590 onwards by the merchants who built cellars and curing places from Cawsand round to Portwrinkle, where the fishermen had bases close to the fishing-ground and cut out the three-mile sail across the Sound to land their catch.

Always fishermen reach out further and further for the richest, less depleted grounds. East Coast men were off Iceland as early as the twelfth century. John Cabot came back to Bristol in 1497 to tell of untold wealth of fish off the new-found land and within a short time the South Devon fishermen were reaching out across the Atlantic. Geographically they were as well-placed to exploit these grounds as the East Coast men had been to exploit the Arctic waters. Plymouth accounts refer to the Newfoundland men as early as 1543. By then the rich fishing grounds of Torbay were yielding four times as much local fish to Brixham, Paignton and Marychurch as Sutton was taking, so the new trade was a godsend to Plymouth and its tradition of bigger ships. The Danes placed an embargo on the English fishing off Iceland at the end of the century, which opened the English markets to Newfoundland fish even more, and gave Plymouth and Dartmouth (its great rival in the trade) an enormous advantage. Their fleets trebled.

Dartmouth from Waterhead Creek, Kingswear. Dartmouth was still a centre for the Newfoundland Trade when William Payne painted this scene (See Chapter 7) (West Country Studies Library)

Sutton Pool and the Barbican: Winter, William Gibbons, (1860–81), oil on canvas (City of Plymouth Museums and Art Gallery)

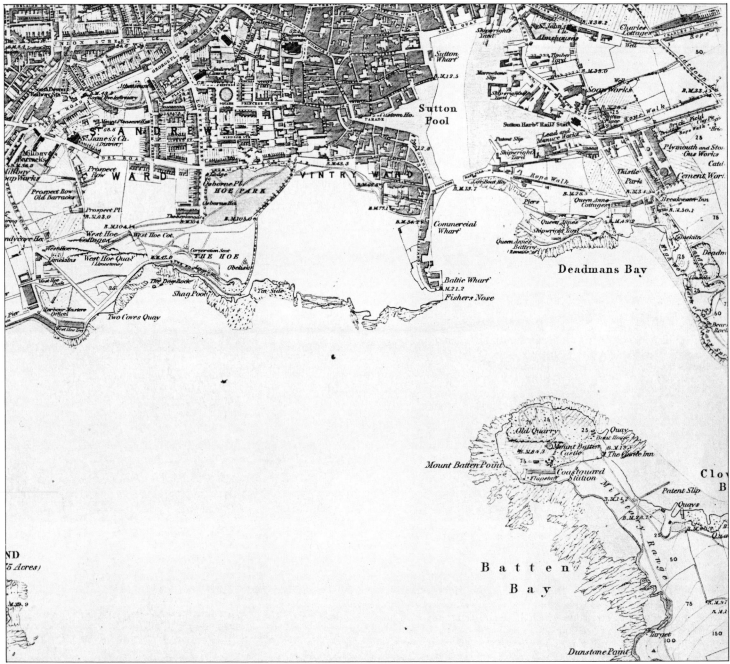

Map of Sutton Pool, Plymouth (Six-inch Ordnance Survey)

The ships sailed from Sutton and the other west harbours on 1 March, normally vessels of about a hundred tons with a crew of about forty men. They came home at the end of September; Plymouth records show fifty Newfoundland craft in port in the autumn of 1595, with two million fish aboard and Dutch and French merchants waiting to buy them. At that time the war with Spain was still in full cry and had given the Devon men an excuse to clear all foreign fishermen off the Grand Banks. By the end of the war in 1603 most ships were sailing their cargoes straight to Spain and Portugal at the end of the season to a ready market.

From 1615 onwards, when the banks had been fished for a century, new grounds were opened off the 'maine' of North America. Plymouth merchants set up fishing bases in the islands off the coast, as they had in Newfoundland, and fishermen could make three times as much money off New England as off Newfoundland. A 1630 writer says that one could often see a hundred sail of the fishing fleet at Plymouth, sometimes two hundred. In 1641, just before the outbreak of the Civil War, Plymouth declared that it was chiefly dependent on the fish trade. But as the colony of Massachusetts grew from 1630 onward so did the English fishermen lose those grounds, and the Civil War really put an end to the English fishing on the New England coast.

The shut-down of this business, and the Siege, hit Plymouth badly. Whereas in 1631 it was sending sixty ships across the Atlantic, which means about 2400 men, compared with Dartmouth's eighty, in 1652 Plymouth had only five ships out against Dartmouth's thirty-four. The trade recovered towards the end of the century but new methods required more capital. The richer merchants of London and Exeter were taking over, and Plymouth's share gradually fell away until it was down to a dozen ships by 1700. It was a less profitable trade, however, than in its early days (in the mid-century Plymouth and Dartmouth men in the business reckoned they were losing 6 per cent a year). The men of Sutton Pool were finding straight trade across the Atlantic more profitable, and the new Dockyard was opening fresh opportunities.

The inshore fishermen of Sutton Harbour had a new fillip when the turnpike roads in the mid-eighteenth century made communication with the rest of England easier. This local fishing had never ceased; W.G. Maton in his *Observations on the Western Counties* of 1794-6 said Plymouth had 'a great exportation of pilchards to Italy and other Catholic countries'. In 1796 William Marshall's *Rural Economy of the West of England* reported 'the market of Plymouth has long, I believe, been esteemed the first in the Island for the abundance, variety, and excellency of its sea fish. Of late years, however, this market has been worse supplied, as the prime fish caught by the fishermen in its vicinity, have been contracted for, by dealers, for that of Bath. And some share of the finny treasure, which these shores produce, is sent, I understand, to the London market'.

Trawling started at about this time with Brixham the pioneer; and by 1820 there were thirty sailing trawlers working out of Sutton Pool. Then the railways gave the harbour a boost. Plymouth was connected

Photograph from an original painting 'Packing Mackerel for the London Market on Plymouth Barbican', c.1840 (Plymouth City Museum). The artist, James Harris, included himself, at the left of the picture with his hand raised to his hat. The lady was Mrs Nash (West Devon Record Office)

Trawler at the Barbican steps, Sutton Pool, 1884. The photograph has been taken from an original painting by W. Gibbons

by main line with London by 1848, twenty years before a branch line reached Brixham. By 1850 Sutton Harbour had sixty trawlers in its fleet of eighty fishing boats, with another two or three hundred craft coming in for the pilchard and mackerel season. In one day alone half a million mackerel were brought in and sold for about £2000. In the first twelve days of March 1850 nearly 400 tons of mackerel was dispatched by rail. By 1862 nearly 2000 tons of fish was sent off by rail, and by 1872 there were sixty-six first class trawlers averaging 34 tons. Plymouth had usurped Brixham's place as Devon's major fishing port.

All this fish was handled on the Barbican, for by law the only permitted wholesale fish market was in Sutton Harbour. The trade doubled between 1878 and 1888. In exceptional times there would be 300 fishing boats in harbour, and 400 or 500 handcarts on the quay waiting to handle the catches. One Lowestoft merchant bought £1000 worth of fish there a week. More fish came from Cornish ports by rail into Millbay, and other fishing boats landed there to avoid the congestion (and the dues) of Sutton Harbour; all this fish was brought through the streets of the town by handcart. The Sutton Harbour men who paid their £1 a year resented what they called G.W.R. fish, and on one occasion, in something like a riot, it was all thrown into the harbour. The fishermen could be rough customers too. A fight delevoped into such proportions one night that the Mayor, as chief magistrate, went down with the constables. He boarded one fishing boat whose crew promptly cast off the lines and began sailing him out through the pierheads. Order was eventually restored and the Mayor set safely ashore.

The Barbican then was a narrow quay barely thirty paces from the front of the houses to the water's edge. A line of cobbles parallel to the houses and laid at right angles to the others still marks the old sea wall. All the shipping agents, the railway companies, the fish merchants and the like had their offices on the quay, to add to the confusion, and something like 4000 people a year embarked at West Pier for ships in the Cattewater and the Sound. Often of a morning their cabs could get no further than the Navy Hotel, where whole families would have to dismount, find a porter for their luggage, and battle as best they could over the cobbles between the piles of fish the shouting auctioneers and the packed buyers, the fisherman and the porters, the handcarts and the buckets.

So in 1889 the Sutton Harbour Improvement Company secured an Act of Parliament entitling them to build a new fish market. The company had discussed it for years, and Plymouth Corporation had gone so far as to have plans drawn up to build a fish market on Commercial Wharf. It came to nothing because the fishermen wanted to be inside the harbour piers. When the Improvement Company sought its Bill the Corporation actually opposed it, on the grounds that such revenues ought not to accrue to private profit, but be used to reduce the tolls on the fishermen. The Corporation even persuaded the House of Lords to incorporate into the final Act a clause that Plymouth should have the right to buy out the new market as soon as the company had built it, but the town did not

exercise its option and the time limit ran out many years ago. The Great Western Railway also entered the list against the Bill, but they appeared as plain straightforward business rivals. The new Act renewed the company's authority to buy the harbour, which marked a vast step forward, and because the market was built out over the bed of the harbour, in front of the Barbican, it was on company land whereas before the company had been renting the quay from the Corporation, and been getting back in return less revenue than they were paying out.

The new market was not actually opened until 1 February 1896 and an extension of time had to be obtained from Parliament. While building operations were in progress the Parade was used for the fish auctions and that led to a new row. Because there was only earth, not cement, between the cobbles there, the fish slime soaked down into the earth, and not only produced an abominable smell but entered the storm water chamber under the Parade and built up so much sewer gas that the manhole covers were forced up. The ventilator in the middle of the Parade, now carrying a lamp on top, was an expedient to deal with the nuisance, and survives as a memeorial to the temporary 1893-5 fish market.

The new fish market was built not just to meet the complaints about congestion in the old, but also to meet a new fishing boom. In 1885 Plymouth sent 3598 tons of fish away by rail, in 1890 the figure was 5159 tons. The 1886 value was £85 851, the 1890 value £162 900, with more fish to the value of £13 000 coming by rail from the Cornish ports to the Plymouth market. No wonder the handcarts from Millbay to Sutton were a nuisance. The peak year was 1892 with 7352 tons of fish landed.

But already the industry was changing – steam trawling had started in the North Sea, resulting in vast catches which not only began to put the sailing smacks out of business but increasingly led to the concentration of the industry in a few large ports. It also meant over-fishing in the North Sea and by the turn of the century the new steam trawlers were reaching back to the rich and historic Arctic grounds. The first locally-owned steam trawler, the *Reginald*, arrived in 1896. She had a red funnel abaft the wheelhouse. Within a decade there were five locally-owned steam trawlers and the firm of Chant and Paddon had been specially formed to operate them.

Sail trawling out of Plymouth was beginning to fail. The boom was over. By 1900 the value of fish landed was cut back to £101 000 and by 1904 was down to £72 000. The fishing industry was described as distressed. It is of course an industry that depends on the supply of fish in the sea; if the fish are not there all the efforts and the capital spent are to no avail, and fish are migratory creatures of changing habits. Chant and Paddon had built their own coal store and maintenance depot on the end of Bayly's Wharf, across the harbour, but they complained that the Sutton Harbour Company had let a coal firm build a big store right alongside which hampered their boats and their trade. The company was willing to build Chant and Paddon a special wharf for their exclusive use if they would double the number of their steam trawlers (at their height they had seven, but one was wrecked on the French coast). In the state of fishing the firm could not do this, and the deadlock remained until the outbreak of war in 1914.

With the rise of the steam trawlers fish became cheaper and more plentiful, and the fish and chip shop was born. In turn their demand for cheap fish led to a new trade, and new problems, in Plymouth. Dogfish, which had been thrown overboard or given to the crew, and generally cursed as a nuisance, became marketable in Plymouth about 1905 and the small hookers which had previously been laid up in the winter months found it profitable to catch them by line. But, because over half a dogfish is thrown away, the offal problem in the market grew considerably. Plymouth Corporation had removed all fish waste until 1906 but, no doubt disturbed by the vast increase in quantities, then refused to move any more. An enterprising character started the Plymouth Fish Guano and Oil Company in a waterside shed at Mount Batten, whence he carted the offal by barge, and by steam process made it into fertilizer. The smell with a southerly wind was so bad that complaints even came from Mutley, a mile away, and in 1912 an injunction shut down the factory. The Improvement Company also passed a by-law forbidding the gutting of fish in the market. But with forty to sixty hookers 'dogging', the by-law was not over-enforced and the Batten factory was revived.

The 1914-18 war and its demands for food kept the trade going which was especially important when Admiralty restrictions virtually limited fishing to close inshore. When the Admiralty took over Mount Batten in 1917 to set up a Royal Naval Air Station, the guano factory finally went out of business. The Improvement Company had to enforce their 'no-gutting' by-law in self-defence, and in December 1917 the fishermen refused to go to sea, saying they could not gut their fish afloat in their small boats. A compromise was reached, that the company would supply bins into which the men would gut on the quay, and they would take the bins to sea on their next trip and empty them.

By 1919 there were 30 000 to 40 000 dogfish – or flake as they were now politely called – being landed on average every day through November to February, and the resulting offal was about twenty-five tons a day. The company tried to enforce its by-law, which the fishermen refused to observe, and a test case was taken to the Plymouth magistrates. Isaac Foot fought the fishermen's case and won, so the company appealed. The Lord Chief Justice, the great Lord Reading, sent the case back to the magistrates for more evidence, and as they examined possible alternatives to the fish market for gutting, Isaac Foot was ironically suggesting the use of Princess Square, the heart of the lawyers' quarter, and even Guildhall Square. Henry Turner appeared for the company and the chairman of the Plymouth magistrates was Lovell Dunstan, a Southside Street ship's chandler and later leader of the Council: quite a collection of Sutton Pool worthies. In January 1920 the Lord Chief Justice, sitting with Mr Justice Avory and Mr Justice Sankey and solemnly debating the time it took a man to clean a dogfish, found that the by-law was unreasonable. But there was also an injunction in Chancery, where

Mr Justice Russell said he thought the by-law not unreasonable, but in view of the higher court's decision he would agree with them. This encouraged the company to go to appeal, and the Master of the Rolls finally found in their favour.

One effect of the new dogfish business of the pre-war days was that the annual number of landings from sailing craft doubled, from 320 in 1907 to 654 in 1913, while the steam trawler landings fell away from 283 in 1909 to 179 in 1913. The war virtually stopped fishing from larger vessels and when a French trawler discharged a load of dogfish in 1919 it was the first steam trawler to discharge in Sutton Harbour for three and a half years. But the long rest had benefited the fishing-grounds. The stocks had built up during the war and the herring shoals, always uncertain migrants, were back. In the winter of 1919-20 there were a hundred steam and motor drifters working out of Plymouth, in from Yarmouth, Lowestoft and the Cornish ports. In one night half a million fish were landed, including 40 000 mackerel and some dogfish.

For the next ten years Plymouth catches increased steadily, until by 1930 Plymouth handled more fish than Newlyn, which had been the premier West Country fishing port since the turn of the century. The trawl and line catches remained fairly constant, but the drifters, catching pilchards, mackerel and herrings, showed the real improvement. In the winter of 1927-28 there were seventy-seven East Coast drifters, as well as the Cornish fleet. The two-month season yielded nearly 123 000 cwt of herrings, three times as much as the trawler yield of 39 000 cwt for the whole year. Special trains where chartered to carry the herrings, and the German and Dutch trawlers were 'klondiking', exporting the fresh fish to Europe.

Scottish and East Coast 'herring lassies' were brought down year after year to deal with the fish on the quayside, and some of them kippered the herrings over fires of mahogany chips in a store at the back of New Street. there are some lively tales told about them.

The peak year was 1930, when 24 000 crans were landed, valued at £66 000. Thereafter a steady decline set in, broken only by one good year in 1932. The western men spotted the decline before the East Coast men; 1931 saw 177 Cornish boats fishing out of Plymouth but after that year their numbers fell away to a handful. On the other hand the East Coast drifters using the port increased in number each year up to the record of 105 in 1936, but the catch that year was only half what the visiting fifty-four East Coast drifters in 1930 shared. But they took the point; next year only fifty-six East Coast boats came down, in 1938 only three, and they have not been seen since.

From 1919 to 1939 the trawl fishing remained fairly static, with peak years in 1934 and 1935. In 1938 Sutton Harbour was the base of thirteen steam trawlers, its largest steam fleet ever. Mr J.G. Wilson owned the *Trojan* and *Oakwold*, both built on the East Coast in the 1890s; Percy Turner owned the *Condor*; Plymouth Trawlers Ltd (Mr John Chant was a director, and the firm in direct descent from the pre-war Chant and Paddon) owned *Sea Hawke, Dereske, Eastbourne* and *Atlantic*; Sanders Stevens owned *Stormcock* and *Verity*, and Mr W. Nicholls owned the *Elk*. A new company, Plymouth Mutual Steam

Fishing Co., was formed with Mr W.J.W. Modley, of Bigwood's Ice Factory, as chairman. They bought three more trawlers in Hull, which Plymouth Trawlers Ltd managed for them. But the smacks were disappearing fast; the 1930 fleet of seventeen had fallen to six by 1934 and after 1937 there was only one in the port. She too went out of commission with the outbreak of war.

Fishing kept up reasonably well for the duration of the war, with the hooker fleet only falling from forty-two boats in 1939 to twenty-nine by 1945. For most of the war years there were seven steam trawlers in the port, but as they had killed the sailing smacks, so the new diesel motor craft were to put them out of business. The steamers slowly disappeared with the last one, Percy Turner's *Perverus*, fishing her last season in 1954. She was the last steam trawler on the South Coast.

During the war the Admiralty had designed and built a large fleet of what they called motor fishing vessels, MFVs, as maids-of-all-work. When they were released at the end of the war they altered not only the motive-power but the appearance of the fishing fleets, resembling neither the old steamers nor the traditional smacks, killing the local traditions in fishing boat designs and substituting a single pattern across the whole country. They did not keep the monopoly, however, and the appearance of the Plymouth fleet today is as varied as it ever was.

But a long decline set in. The 37 500 cwt of fish landed in 1947 was just about the same as the trawler landings of twenty years before. By 1963, although the number of large fishing boats had increased from six to eight, the catch was down to 8000 cwt. In spite of the rise in money values, the 1963 catch yielded only £44 000 against the £89 000 of 1947. Then a slow recovery began. By 1968 the catch had increased by 50 per cent to 12 500 cwt, valued at £82 000, and there were fourteen first-class boats at work. During this time the proportion of the catches of the western ports had changed. Newlyn, which had been a little higher in 1947, was showing treble the Plymouth figure by 1968, and Brixham, which had begun to overtake Plymouth in the late 1930s, was landing double the amount in 1968. One vital development in Plymouth, however, was the shellfishing, which between the wars was still left to the fishing villages. In 1947 Plymouth shellfish were worth £3000, but by 1968 this had risen to £23 500, in addition to the wet fish returns. So the total value of fish landings, wet and shell, for 1968 amounted to £105 105.

But a real boom came after 1967, when British territorial waters were extended from three to twelve miles. This kept the big Russian fishing fleets as well as the individual Frenchmen and Belgians off the valuable inshore grounds. At the same time Sutton Harbour spent £25 000 on improving the fish market services. Diesel fuel is now available alongside and Bigwoods (now Plymouth Cold Store Ltd), ice merchants in the port since 1789, installed a new ice plant in a building specially constructed by the Sutton Harbour company, from which ice can be tipped by chute straight into the holds. So the turn-round of the fishermen was speeded, and a new range of offices for the fish salesmen and the Ministry of Agriculture and Fisheries

replaced the old wooden huts. The market remains structurally the same, looking like a lost railway station under its Victorian roof, but it was geared for the boom.

Other factors helped. New gear was developed for catching pelagic fish – mackerel, pilchards and herrings – and world markets were opening up for shellfish, not just crabs and lobsters but scallops and queen scallops. By 1974 there were 114 fishing vessels registered at Plymouth with another thirty craft over 40 feet in the Plymouth-Cawsand fleet using Sutton Harbour exclusively. Even bigger vessels from Teignmouth, Brixham, the Channel Islands and Scotland work out of the Pool for a long winter season, with smaller craft from other South Devon and Cornish ports. In 1975 Brixham and Torbay Fish Ltd, a fishermen's cooperative, took over the quayside ice plant and planned to expand production. To cope with the heavy landings more quay space had to be found, and pelagic fish – mainly mackerel – are now landed at Bayly's Wharf and Lockyer Quay at Coxside, sometimes up to 300 tons a day. New suction methods empty the holds at high speed. Live storage tanks for crabs and lobsters have also been established there. The scallop landings have led to fish processing factories being opened at Saltash and Buckfastleigh. In 1970 the Sutton Harbour company also bought Bigwood's old freezing plant in Citadel Ope, installed new deep-freeze equipment, and a shellfish processing factory there exports their products to the United States and Europe.

Fish exports have developed considerably, partly through Britains's entry into the Common Market. Mackerel goes to France, Holland and Germany, pilchards to Belgium, bass and monkfish to France, crabs to Sweden, and most of the scallops and queens to the United States. In 1976 a new trawler joined the fleet, planning to catch horse mackerel for an African market.

In round figures the 12 000 cwt of pelagic fish landed at Plymouth in 1970 had risen to over 68 000 cwt in 1973 and leapt to 177 000 cwt by 1974. Against this Plymouth's handling of the more expensive demersal fish, such as plaice and soles, which remained fairly constant between 8000 and 9000 cwt in the early 1970s, fell to under 6000 cwt in 1974. So that while Plymouth is now landing in weight more fish than its old rivals, Newlyn and Brixham, put together, the total value of its 1974 catch was £389 000 against Newlyn's £877 000 and Brixham's £709 000. But Sutton Harbour is advancing faster than any other fishing port in the west. The provisional figures for 1975 showed 372 000 cwt valued at £1 060 000 landed. Only Newlyn in the west showed a higher value. Scallops made nearly a third of the Sutton valuation figure.

This may still be small beer against the returns of the deep-sea fishing ports, but it is locally important. There are over fifty shore workers in the trade on the Barbican alone, and all told the fishing out of Sutton Harbour may employ up to 600 people. In the autumn of 1975 there were signs of the herring returning so the pressure on quay space may yet increase. The current boom has already passed in tonnage the previous peak of 1892 but fish come and go. The new methods could be sweeping the grounds so cleanly that there may be state-imposed limitations, or even the fall-off in catches that follows over-fishing. But Sutton Harbour has been stimulated by a boom in its oldest industry at a time of world depression.

Pilchards, Fortifications and Trawlers

Pilchards, by tradition one of Cornwall's three staple commodities, were hardly less important to Plymouth during the sixteenth and seventeenth centuries. The governments of the period anxiously learnt not only of the impact of the Spanish threat on the fishery, but also of the transfer of the fishery's centre from Plymouth to Cawsand on the Cornish side of the Sound.

The direct answer to the Spanish threat was to build a fort above Sutton Harbour at Fisher's Nose, on a site now partly occupied by the present Citadel. The link between this fort and the fishing industry is explained in a pamphlet[1] produced on the occasion of the 1961 Fishing Feast by the former Archivist at Plymouth City Library. A 'toll' on pilchards landed in Devon and Cornwall raised the sum of £877 between 1592 and 1595. This was enough to make a significant contribution to the cost of the fort, and the 'toll' enough to cause a fall in landings at Plymouth (where it was enforced) and a rise at the Cornish ports (where it was not).

Plymouth was now provided with improved defences, and with the new garrison, an increased population. This circumstance made worse the remaining problem of loss of food supplies in the area. The Plymouth merchants, and indeed the town as a whole, had been affected by the growth of Cawsand as a fishing centre, and this is mentioned both in Crispin Gill's work[2] and in an article by Professor A.L. Rowse.[3] For some twenty years the Privy Councils of Elizabeth I and James I received conflicting petitions from the Cawsand and Plymouth factions. Typically, what caused them most concern was the export of fish cargoes, and any contracts likely to restrict 'open market' sales. In 1588, 'Armada year', Drake was himself appointed one of the Commissioners to control these activities. Referred to, but not printed by Rowse, is further evidence from 1606, now preserved at the West Devon Record Office. It is in the form of Privy Council instructions closely copying the terms of the earlier Commission and alleging that the end of the war with Spain will make them easier to obey.[4]

1. That two third parts of the pilchards taken at or neere about Cawston Baie may be brought to Plymouth, Stonehouse, Milbrooke and Saltashe, and that of the said two third parts the one halfe at the leaste may be brought to Plymouth and there sold to the Townesmen and Countrie people such as shall be there to buy them.
2. That noe person shall make any agreement before hand with any takers of pilchards or with any owners of Saynes or Boats used therin for any [of] the said fish with entent to transporte the same beyond the Seas.

3. That from hensforth noe manner of person dwelling out of the said Counties of Devon and Cornwall shall have any sellars [cellars] in Cawston or uppon the Clifes thereaboutes to be used for saving of any of the said pilchards.
4. That noe pilchards taken in an about Cawston Baie be transported out of this realme but in vessels belonging to some of the portes within the said two Counties of Devon and Cornwall.
5. That noe drift netts be used for the taking of pilchards within the points of the land more than Two dayes in every weeke viz: Tuesday and Thursday.

The Privy Council's wishes were duly transmitted by the agency of a committee which met at Launceston on 13 August 1606.[5] It was composed of Sir Ferdinando Gorges (governor of the fort), Sir William Strode (of Newnham), Sir Anthony Rous, Richard Carew of Antony, Sir Christopher Harris (of Radford) and James Bagg (the Mayor of Plymouth), all men with strong local connections. Instructions were given to the Constables of the parishes of Rame, Maker, St John's, Sheviock and Antony to warn all owners and masters of seines and boats to meet at Saltash by 'nine of the clocke in the morning' on Saturday, 16 August. A note is added to the memorandum to certify that the gathering was duly held and that the seine and boat owners agreed to the orders passed on to them.

Perhaps the most visible monument to Plymouth's place in the fishing industry of the nineteenth century is the Marine Biological Laboratory's building beneath the Citadel on the Hoe. Its site, served by what was then, as now, the largest centre of population south-west of Bristol, and the middle of the three most considerable fishing ports in Cornwall and Devon (the others being Newlyn and Brixham), was chosen with some care.[6]

Lysons' work on Devon mentions that there were forty trawlers in Plymouth by the year 1822.[7] Yet by 1830 only eighteen out of 390 baptisms at St Andrews's Church were of fishermen's children (none seem to have come from Charles).[8] This very modest figure points perhaps to the youth of the fishing crews as a class; they were either too young to have children of their own or could not afford to be married. This was certainly a feature of the Brixham crews seventy years later as the register on page 13 shows.

By 1850 there were sixty trawlers, as Crispin Gill mentions. At this later date, Census Enumerator's Returns (1851–81) exist which show the origins of the fishing community and locality of their homes. At a period when Brixham men were migrating eastwards, these returns show that both fishermen and dealers from Kent and London were migrating westwards to Plymouth. Typical locations for their homes were High Street, St Andrew's Street, Castle Street and Stokes Lane.[9]

As the nineteenth century advanced, Plymouth and Brixham, relying on their trawlers, and Newlyn, relying on the traditional Cornish seine nets, vied for leadership among the fishing ports of the South West. The railway reached Plymouth significantly ahead of its

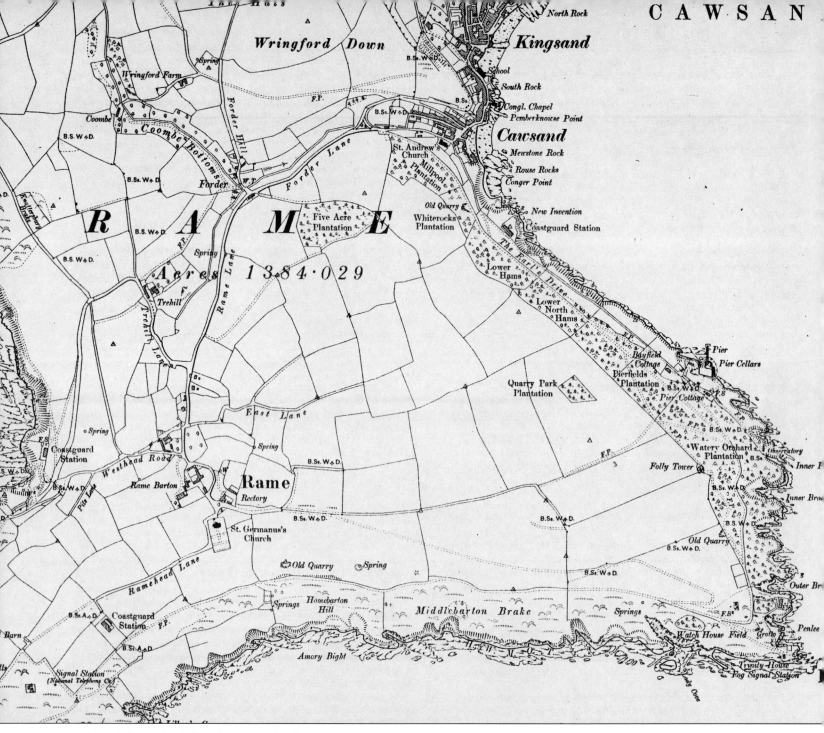

Kingsand, Cawsand and Pier Cellars (Six-inch Ordnance Survey)

When Baptized.	Child's Christian Name.	Parents' Names. Christian.	Surname.	Abode.	Quality, Trade, or Profession.	By whom the Ceremony was performed.
BAPTISMS solemnized in the Parish of *Lower Brixham* in the County of *Devon* in the Year One thousand eight hundred and *Ninety Eight*						
1898 Oct 29 No. 1193	Gilbert	Gilbert & Sarah	Bird	Lower Brixham	Fisherman	Fred Godden
1898 Sept 13 No. 1194	Ella Elizabeth	William Henry & Charlotte	Edmunds	Lower Brixham	Fisherman	Fred Godden
1898 Nov 4 No. 1195	George Albert	John & Rosa	Perrott	Lower Brixham	Fisherman	Fred Godden
1898 Nov 4 No. 1196	Augusta Louisa	George William & Catherine	Windeatt	Lower Brixham	Fisherman	Fred Godden
1898 Nov 5 No. 1197	William Janfield Beer	Robert Alfred Beer & Sarah Ann	Towell	Lower Brixham	Fisherman	Fred Godden
1898 Nov 6 No. 1198	Frederick William Seat	William & Mary Alberta	Treeby	Lower Brixham	Fisherman Farmer	Fred Godden
1898 Nov 6 No. 1199	Blanch Rotina	Henry Leonard & Irena	Lewis	Lower Brixham	Fisherman Mason	Fred Godden
1898 Nov 8 No. 1200	Lydia Marjory	Edward Albert & Lydia	Mitchell	Lower Brixham	Fisherman Carpenter	Fred Godden

Slips of the pen by Frederick Godden, Curate of All Saints, Lower Brixham. All Saints was the fishermen's church founded by the Rev. H.F. Lyte in 1826 (All Saints, Brixham, Parish Records)

rivals, but there were progressive improvements at Newlyn (where the breakwater was completed in 1896). Ironically, Brixham's breakwater was finally completed only in 1921, when the great days of the 'smacks' were over, but more modest improvements had continued there during the later nineteenth century. Another feature of the developing industry was the dependence on 'foreign' ports of fishing fleets far from home, and Scottish and East Coast fleets took full advantage of the increased shelter and handling facilities as they became available.

The fishing boats of this period and the trips they made can be followed in some detail among the Shipping Registers and Returns of Fishing Boats. The following items give some idea of the inter-dependence (as well as the more-publicized rivalry) between ports of the South West.[10]

The *Dew Drop*, a two-masted lugger of 18 tons, was built at Newlyn in 1871 and sold in 1875 to J.S. Paddon, fish salesman of Plymouth. (He was doubtless a founder of the firm which later owned steam trawlers.)

The *Oimara*, a 49-ton sloop built at Brixham in 1872, had a somewhat more varied career. Also sold to J.S. Paddon, fish salesman, and to James Callard, fisherman, both of Plymouth. She was altered to ketch rig in 1889, sold to a Lowestoft owner (and shortly after broken up!) in 1902.

The *Esmeralda*, a 32-ton cutter, was built at Plymouth by David Banks and Co. and sold to Philip Hingston, fisherman. She appears to have remained at Plymouth.

— 2 —
START BAY
CRABS AND CRAB BAIT

As recently as the years following the Second World War any gastronomic handbook to Devon must surely have included the Start Bay crabs, large and succulent. The story behind the crateloads of hissing, impotently-scraping crustaceans sent to market has been examined by two researchers in the field in the last days of the traditional fishery.

Professor Melvin Firestone of Arizona State University visited Hallsands in 1974-5 and was able to make an in-depth study of the structure and activities of the fishing community there.

Dorothy Wright went to Beesands in 1963 and recorded the traditional and more modern methods of making crab pots there.

Professor Firestone's study originally appeared in *Folk Life*, a magazine of anthropological studies. His work, revealing to outsiders the complex sequence of work to catch the bait with which to bait the crab pots, has already been reprinted locally in Devon. In another study, published in the United States, he has examined the pattern of crew membership and boat ownership among the older Hallsands men and drawn interesting parallels with smaller (cod-trap) boats in certain areas of Newfoundland. His acknowledgements are as follows.

This paper is a revised version of 'The Traditional Start Bay Crab Fishery' which appeared in *Folk Life*, Volume 20, 1982.

The research upon which this paper is based was carried out during 1974-75 while on sabbatical from Arizona State University as a visiting scholar at the Department of Maritime Studies of the University of Wales Institute of Science and Technology. I thank these organizations for their support and encouragement. Alastair Couper of the latter institution, and Peter Fricke, in the Department at the time, deserve special thanks. I owe a deep debt of gratitude to many in South Devon for their aid and interest; to mention but a few: Perce, Jim, and Allen Trout of Hallsands; Nora Stone of Hallsands; Mr and Mrs Perce Tolchard of Bickerton; Cyril Stone of Kellaton; and to the late Alfred Hutchings of Beesands. My thanks also go to Robert

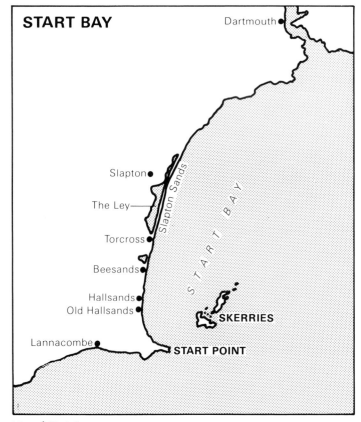

Map of Start Bay

Pim of the Department of Extra-mural Studies of the University of Exeter; to Kay Coutin, then with the Department of Extra-mural Studies; to W.H. Williams of the Department of Fisheries, Plymouth; and Rev. T.J. Jones of Stokenham. I am grateful to Dr R.J.F. Pinsent of the Royal College of General Practitioners, of Birmingham; and to Sheila Pimm Jolly of West Ewell, Surrey for allowing me to quote her manuscript. But my heartiest thanks to Sharon Firestone of Tempe, Arizona.

The Technology of the Traditional Start Bay Crab Fishery first describes the area and the history of its involvement with fishing. It recalls the dredging of the Skerries Bank and the destruction of old Hallsands during the winter of 1903–1904. Reprinted here is the core of the article embodying Professor Firestone's studies 'in the field'.

The Start Bay Crab Fishery

Technology

Next follows a description of the various types of fishing equipment, and their use, in the traditional crab fishery in Hallsands, Beesands and Lannacombe. It should be noted that most of this equipment was not used for catching crabs, but for catching bait with which to catch crabs, or for catching other fish to sell. Crab pots needed to be baited with fish that would not readily disintegrate while in the water and fall off the skewers by which they were fastened. Such fish were usually taken by longlines (particularly after the First World War with the disappearance of tuck netting) but other fish, themselves 'too soft' to be used for crab bait, were usually obtained by seining and used as bait on longlines. Apart from this, bait was purchased from passing trawlers and sometimes supplied by those purchasing crabs; all of which made for a complicated and arduous fishing schedule. Not all this equipment was used in each of the communities. Lannacombe had no beach along which fish could be netted and so fishermen from there seined with a crew from Hallsands. On the other hand, Torcross and Slapton, the communities to the north of Beesands, were not involved in the crab fishery but did seine and tuck netting and other forms of fishing in the past.

The implications for the social structure of such labour-intensive equipment are obvious. The two-man 'boat-crews' involved in the catching of crabs were directly related to the exigencies of the enterprise, and the larger 'seine crews' which supplied the increased number of men required for netting were composed of a number of boat crews who shared in the fish taken. Seine crews usually consisted of four boat crews and had the following activities in common:

1. Fishing for bait with a seine net. This was 'shot' from the shore out to sea and returned surrounding a school of fish. These were sighted by a 'hillman' stationed upon a nearby height who then directed the paying out of the net by hand signals. The seine boat was rowed by three men and a fourth 'shot the net'. Wives helped

Second edition of the six-inch Ordnance Survey map of 1885, showing Hallsands

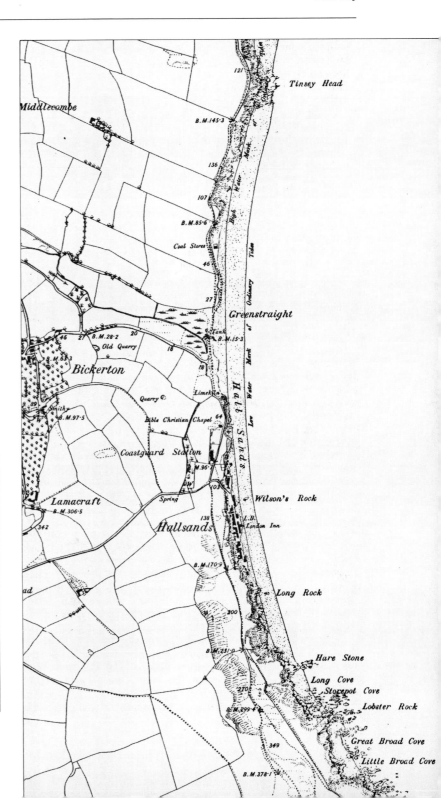

haul the seine and received two-thirds of a share of the catch each. Men received one share with three shares going to the owner of the net and boat. Bait was shared equally between boat crews while proceeds of fish sold were divided according to the above share system.

2. Maintaining a common winch for hauling boats out of the water, mutual aid in launching and hauling boats (others in the community would also help) and fishing in company for safety. Longlining would be done in concert to ensure that lines would not become tangled.

3. Some seine crews maintained willow groves for the making of crab pots.[1]

That such groups were largely agnatic reflects a general tendency of inshore fishermen in the North Atlantic.[2] The existence of tuck netting with its large crews in the past undoubtedly contributed to community integration, particularly in the face of the numerous tourists swarming the beaches in the summer. The story is told of the old fisherman at Torcross who would throw squid at tourists who were pressing so close as to interfere with net hauling, and Fitzgibbon[3] shows tourists staring at fish being landed at Slapton Sands at the turn of the century.

Tuck nets (tuck seines)

'Tuck net' or 'tuck seine' are local terms. The general term for this device is a 'drag net'. In Hallsands, Beesands and Torcross there were, up through the First World War, and in Slapton in the past, tuck nets with which groundfish such as plaice, dabs, and whiting were caught. These fish were used for crab bait and were consumed by the fisherman. This was not a matter of surrounding a shoal of fish when sighted as with the seine net, but of dragging an area for groundfish to get whatever was there. Both the net and the attached ropes frightened the fish and drove them toward shore. This device was employed within the lifetime of the grandfather of a man giving evidence to a Sea Fisheries Commission in 1863.[4] The following description is of the use of this device at Beesands within the life of an elderly fisherman, now but a few years deceased.

The craft employed was a 'hauling boat' rowed by six men. It contained the net and attached ropes. The former was 20 fathoms long and the attached ropes were 'cables' of 15 fathoms each. These were attached to wooden 'balancers' at the end of the net running between the top and bottom of the net. The attempt was to keep the balancers upright when pulling in the net. As the device caught groundfish, the top of the net was under water and the ropes were of 1½-inch Russian hemp, Stockholm tarred, so as to sink.

The device was payed out so as to form somewhat of a rhomboid with the shoreline at the bottom, the ropes the sides, and the net the top. A rectangle was not formed because the rope was 'payed out' from shore in a way to 'stem the tide'; that is, not to run perpendicularly from the shore but at a slight angle into the direction of the tidal flow. This was to help compensate for the tidal flow so

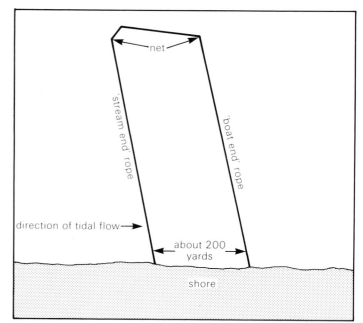

Method of casting out a tuck-net from the shore

that the net would not be pulled downstream ahead of the men on shore pulling it in.

The rope on the side of the tidal flow was called the 'stream end' and the one opposite, the 'boat end'. The stream end, including the cable, was put out at an angle into the tidal flow. The boat then turned away from the tidal flow approximately parallel to the shore and put out the net, the 'boat end cable', and two 'ropes' or 'lengths' of the boat end before turning back to shore. There were two more lengths in the boat end than in the stream end. In pulling the net in, two lengths of the boat end were pulled in before the stream end was begun to be pulled in. This was noted by the 'joins' (where the lengths were tied together) when they came in. When the first two lengths of the boat end were in, a fisherman waved his hand and cried 'bends up!' as a sign that the stream end should be begun to be pulled in. The stream end was harder to pull in and the boat end would tend to 'gain on' the stream end.

The stream end was pulled in by men walking along in the direction of the tidal flow, but the boat end was hauled from the place the boat had put it ashore. The stream end was then brought to the stationary boat end. This moving along with the stream end was called haulin' and fallin' (walking). The rear man of those pulling on a rope coiled it. This was called 'pulling tail'. 'Pulling opposite' or 'keeping stroke', when hauling nets or crab pots, referred to having some crew members pulling on the oposite stroke so as to make for an even pull.

Working a tuck-net from the shore. Although this P.O. Hutchinson picture records an attempt to recover a body from the sea off Sidmouth, it well illustrates the method used for hauling in the net (West Country Studies Library)

During the six hours of ebb tide the flow is southward, parallel to the shore. It flows in the same direction during the first three hours of the flood tide also, and then northward during the second three hours of the flood tide. The fishermen began 'paying out' an hour and a half after the onset of the flood tide and were finished before the tidal flow changed direction and began to flow northwards.

The bunt of the tuck net was 60 feet deep, twice as deep as the arms. When it became worn it was cut in half to make two arm sections. Loops of rope were attached to the bunt to help protect it from wear as it was dragged along. There were leads on the foot ropes and corks on the head ropes and the mesh was 2½ inches. Worn sections of rope were doubled and made into the cables. The ropes in the latter were tied together with overhead knots every 6 inches to keep them together.

Twelve men handled a tuck net, six men on a side. Women were involved in drawing tuck nets ashore in 1863.[5] The catch of a tuck net crew was divided into six lots, one for each group of two fishermen that comprised the crab boat crews. The fish were put into piles and each group of two men 'memorized' a stone. These stones would then be cast on the piles by an outsider and each crab boat crew would have the pile upon which its stone rested. In this way an impartial division of the catch was effected.

In Newfoundland, in the Strait of Belle Isle area, there was a similar custom related to parcelling out an inheritance. Stones would be laid out on the side of a house representing approximately equal portions of property. A boy would then throw a stone representing each inheritor over the roof of the house from the other side. Each inheritor received the portion nearest to which his rock landed. Much of the immigration into that part of Canada was from Devon.[6]

The tuck net was generally owned by the entire crew which operated it; however, as was noted previously, this was not always the case. 'Dead shares' were taken out for maintenance, these amounting to 'just a little' for the men who turned out to dry and care for the nets. 'Tuck netting' is colourfully referred to in a travel book of 1895:

Rows of fishing boats line the beach, and bales of nets are everywhere for the inhabitants of Hallsands are fisher folk. So are they who dwell at Beesands, a smaller hamlet about a mile further on. And the fishing operations are worth watching. I have done some seine fishing myself, and looked on it a great deal more; but I have never seen such a lengthy performance as the seining at these villages. Hundreds of volumes of rope are employed, and half an hour to one – taking no account of the casting of the net – is something of a job. After watching the yards and yards of rope that the two lines of men drag slowly from the sea, and seeing no signs of the net, I enquired the length of the line in use. 'Eight lengths of 60 fathoms apiece, one hand and eleven lengths of 60 fathom t'other', said a son of Zebedee, tranquilly as though a mile or two of rope was nothing at all. Here by degrees, the 2000 odd yards of line comes in hand over hand and is piled in great coils on the beach until suddenly the surface of the water breaks into bubbles and splashes like a great kettle boiling over, and then the seine appears enclosing a struggling mass of fish, the cause of this commotion. Well out of reach of the tide are they drawn, and then in the most business-like manner arranged and sorted, 'the good placed in vessels – i.e. hampers – and the bad cast away'.[7]

Tuck seines which went out even further existed. In 1863 a man from Torcross stated before the Commissioners Appointed to Inquire into the Sea Fisheries of the United Kingdom that they:

'... are put out at a distance from 600 to 800 fathoms from the shore ... We are obliged to go a long way off the shore, The flat-fish do not come close in-shore. Our bay consists principally of large pebbles. We do not get any muddy ground till we get 200 or 300 fathoms from the shore.'[8]

At a later point the same man stated that 'with such nets we sometimes go out for 1400 or 1500 fathoms', and he also stated that the arms of a tuck net were not more than three fathoms deep and that the bunt was not more than 4 or 5 fathoms deep. Contrast this with the larger tuck seine already described for Beesands. Was it that in 1863 tuck seines at Torcross were much smaller and went further out than those employed later at Beesands?

These implements are not to be confused with the tuck seines which were part of pilchard seines used in Cornwall. The latter were circles of nets some 300 fathoms in circumference hauled to shore when a shoal was captured, and there:

'... the net is securely moored, as several days may elapse before all the fish are taken out. This operation is performed with the tuck seine, and is termed 'tucking the fish'. The tuck seine is about 70 fathoms long and 10 fathoms deep with a considerable quantity of slack net to form a bag or bunt in the middle. It is shot like an ordinary seine, but inside the circle made by the other nets, and the two ends are hauled into a boat, leaving the middle of the bunt in the water. The foot-rope of this part of the net is gradually raised up so as to bring the bunt under the fish and lift them to the surface; they are then bailed out with large baskets and taken ashore to be salted.'[9]

The phrase 'tucking the trap' refers in Newfoundland to the emptying of a cod trap. The cod trap is a large square or rectangular box of nets; four sides and a bottom set out for the season in a 'berth'. The trap is tucked by the bottom being taken up from one side of the net to the other so as to form a moving ridge which drives the fish into one end where they are taken out with a dip net.[10]

Seine Nets
Grey mullet were taken in seines and caught through February until the first fortnight in May. They were taken usually during overcast, rainy weather, on the flood tide, with the wind from the south-west or west. A hillman* would watch from the cliffs and direct the fishermen by waving his cap. In 'the old days' the job was considered a speciality and two shares went to the lookout. Later, only one share was given because a man on lookout all day might find that his replacement had sighted a shoal when he was in to eat, and it would not be fair for the replacement to receive his extra share. There was a little watch-house on the heights south of Hallsands where a hillman could take shelter. When a shoal was sighted he would signal to a man waiting on the shore who would shout, 'Aye, boats', as a signal to the rest of the crew to assemble.

The seine net boat ('seine boat') was then put out. These small open boats, pointed at either end, were rowed by three men with a fourth to let out the net. The seine boat was owned by the seine crew as a whole and used only for seining. A seine net boat was kept ready on shore, its net in the rear forming a hump which was covered by a 'cap'. One old boat at Hallsands was called 'The Coconut' because its cap formed a ball. As the net was let out the rocks tied to the bottom had to be set gently into the water lest a splash frighten the fish.

The hillman had to judge the speed of the fish so that he could direct the boat crew to get the seine in front of the shoal before they struck. One end of the seine would be shot around the fish and then back to shore. If the fish struck the net before they were surrounded they would escape. If an alarmed shoal came into contact with another the latter would also move off. Mullet move northward along the coast and so hillmen at Hallsands and Beesands would be posted on heights south of each community. When the fish were surrounded the arms of the net were hauled in. The seine consisted of a deeper central portion called the bunt, and longer shallower sections on each side called the arms. The arm on the side the tide was running was moved towards the other. The fish were secured in the bunt which had a depth of about 35–40 feet and 15 feet at the ends of the arms. (Seines with depths of 13 fathoms at the bunt and lengths of 150 fathoms are mentioned in 1863.)[12] The fishermen did not knit their own nets but purchased sections and sewed them together.

With a light catch a minimum of six people was required to pull in a seine: two on each foot rope (attached to the bottom) and one on each head rope (attached to the top). With a heavy catch men would also get into the water and push against the bunt. This was particularly true in the past when seines were made of cotton. At Hallsands, the seine was operated and shared-in by both men and women of the crews, men getting one share each and women two-thirds of a share each. Before winches were used for this purpose, women helped pull up boats by hand.

If someone had gone away, except on crew business, he did not get a share of the hauls he had missed. Fishermen say that tourists, seeing women hauling the nets, did not feel that the men were putting forth an equal amount of effort when the latter were in the water pushing against the bunt. However, the men's work was the

*In the Cornwall pilchard seining industry these men were called 'huers'.[11]

more arduous, especially as there was a danger of the bottom of the net turning out and fish escaping.

Catches of fish by this method would be about 15 cwt a day. The fish were taken out of the seine with baskets, packed by the crew and picked up by a buyer. The latter would later telegraph them telling how much the fish had brought. If mullet did not bring a significant amount the fishermen did not fish. Grey mullet would keep very well for a few days before being sent out and the crew would pour salt water over them if it did not rain. Mackerel, on the other hand, did not keep well and if caught in the morning spoiled by the afternoon. Seining for mackerel was done in the same manner. In the past, fish, particularly mackerel, was also sold to hawkers who would come with horses and traps and sell the fish to farmers and farm workers. The hawkers would be informed of a catch by the fishermen going out to sea and hoisting a signal that would be seen from Torcross. The hawkers would then arrive to bid on the catch – sometimes before it was completely hauled in.

There were three extra shares in the seine crew for the upkeep of the net and seine boat; if there were twelve men in a crew there would be fifteen shares. Seine crews might also be referred to as 'crowds'. There were two crews of fishermen at Hallsands for seine netting through the 1930s until the Second World War. Each group consisted of four two-man crab boat crews. Besides mullet and mackerel they caught sand eels ('lant' or 'launce'), for which a different net was used. After the Second World War there was only one seine crew largely due to men having been killed in the war and a lack of recruitment to the industry.

Seining continued for mullet and mackerel from South ('Old') Hallsands after the village was destroyed and the fishermen were living in North Hallsands. The women of the crew would then go down to South Hallsands at 5 a.m. At other times they would be at home and someone who had heard the cry 'Aye, boats' would tell them. There was at one time a woman who lived in the Mildmay cottages who took an interest and passed the word. Eventually the boat and net were moved to North Hallsands.

It is said by non-fishermen that in the past 'Beesands would get angry with Hallsands' during the netting season because they felt that the fish came by Hallsands first and the Hallsands fishermen had, in that way, an unfair advantage. Use of seine nets continued until at least 1975 at Beesands. The only hauling of a seine net I observed was there on Sunday afternoon, 13 April 1975. A hillman was out and there was a cry of 'Aye, boats'. There was an air of excitement and anxiety on the beach, dogs were told to stop barking and children to stop running. Two Torcross men were jokingly told to go back there. That same year a boat and net was prepared at Hallsands, but they were not put out.

Sand eels were taken in a seine net with a fine mesh, usually at Torcross. They were used as bait on longlines to catch rays, congers and dogfish as bait for crabs. Sand eel nets were called 'lant nets'. They were stored in boxes which stood on four legs and had handles for carrying. Young[13], says of these fish:

'... one of the best baits is the sand launce or eel. The French fishermen are so well aware of the attractiveness that their boats cross over from Dieppe and other ports to Slapton and Torcross in Start Bay on the south coast of Devon, purposely to purchase the launce, some of the fishermen using fine meshed nets especially to catch and supply these bait to the foreigners; they sell it from twenty pence to two shillings per bushel.'

Longlines ('Bultows')
This was a matter of putting out a line which stretched horizontally near the sea bottom. From this line, which was marked by buoys and held in place by them and at the ground, hung short lines upon which were fastened baited hooks. It was best to do longlining with four in a boat. Two could 'set up' but it took at least three to pull it in, and one to tend the engine. Two men pulled the line in, one pulled and took the fish off, and the other coiled and steered. Putting out the longline was done by three men in two boats. One man put out the line, the other steered (or rowed if there was no engine) and the third stood by in case of tangles. Twelve lines of hooks per longline were used. The snood lines, to which the hooks were attached, were known as 'nausel lines' locally. There was a stone at every thirty hooks to keep the longline at the bottom. It would be left overnight to fish for groundfish in deep water, about three miles out, on a sandbank.

Cod were caught fifty years ago but have now 'moved off'. They were taken with longlines in the autumn and early winter. The heads were used as crab bait but they were also sold for as little as 1d a pound, heads off and gutted. Conger and skate were fished for at night with longlines.

Bait and the Fishing Cycle
The fishermen would seine for sand eels, mullet, ray and turbot The latter was sold and used for bait. Bait was preserved by salting and drying. Mullet and sand eels were not used as crab bait because the flesh was not tough enough to last in the water after being skewered. With the traditional pots the bait was pierced with an 'oush' (hazel) stick which was then stuck in the 'funnel' of the pot. With the newer pots the bait is held in place by an elastic band and not skewered, thus allowing 'softer' fish such as mullet to be used. Sand eels, mullet, ray, turbot, congers, 'gurnot' (gurnards) and sometimes whiting were used for bait in longlines. Gurnards were the best crab bait. Mackerel and herring could not be used in the willow pots as they got too soft and dropped off the skewers, 'but plaice you could gill up all right'. Thus, crabbing involved three different stages of fishing: (1) seining for soft fish which were used as bait for longlines; (2) longlining for more firm fish with which to bait crab pots; and (3) catching the crabs in baited pots. The fact that all these activities had to be engaged in, often in a period of two days, meant a long and arduous work schedule.

The fishermen also used to get gurnards for bait from sailing trawlers that went by. If trawlers had bait to sell they would fly a 'mop' (a white flag) from the stern. Captains would sometimes save bait for their friends and sell only to them. The Hallsands men would race the Beesands men out and compete with them in bidding for the gurnot. Selling the gurnot was a perk of the trawler crew, the skipper got no money for it. It was difficult to tell if a trawler was coming in to sell bait or not — it might just be heading in, tacking. 'Beesands' would see them first, and 'Hallsands' would go out when they saw 'Beesands' go out.

Salmon Nets

Salmon fishing occurred in the past and one had to pay for a licence. Only those with licences could catch salmon legally, and then only with a 4 inch mesh net. One could also not fish for salmon between 7 a.m. on Friday and 6 a.m. on Monday, and there was a bailiff in the area who would enforce these regulations. Salmon nets were inherited from father to son. When salmon were inadvertently caught in the seine nets women had been known to hide them in their aprons and run home with them. The story is told that once a few salmon were caught in a seine and a tourist came by and asked what kind of fish they were; one fisherman present said salmon, but then another fisherman next to him reprimanded him saying, for the benefit of the tourist, that the fish were cod and that it was shocking that he couldn't tell cod after all these years!

Salmon used to be poached. One man was fined for shipping salmon which was marked as other fish as there was a special rate for shipping salmon. He was not fined for poaching, however. The tails of the salmon were displayed at the trial as evidence and it was jokingly said that the judge had eaten the rest.

Other devices

Jiggers were used, particularly for mackerel. They consisted of a lead weight at the end of a line with feathers and hooks on the line above the weight. Trammel nets were used to get fish for bait. These had very wide mesh nets hanging on either side of a smaller meshed net. There was a leaded rope at the bottom and they were about one fathom deep. Before the First World War there were larger herring and pilchard nets that involved all the men in each community of Hallsands and Beesands.

Crab Fishing

The local term for crab fishing is 'potting' and crab fishermen are 'potters'. Lobsters are caught in 'ink-well' pots which are woven of willows by the fishermen. Sail boats were employed in the fishery until the First World War and oars were used when fishing on the grounds. When the motor boats first came in, a sail was used aswell. The sail boats went to about 16 feet and the motor boats generally 18 feet with a 6-foot beam. One of the fishermen described the work.

'We'd use the sails when we had a chance, going to the ground or comin' back, but always work with the oars when we got on the ground. And if the wind freshened up we always carried shingle ballast in bags in the bottom of 'em — for ballast. Cause she had big sails on 'em, you see. And then we shift that ballast from one side to the other when you were going about, workin', comin' in from the fishin'. We store that, when you got on the ground, store it in the boats. See, lay it down, all in place ready to go up again, when you finished. But if you didn't have no wind you had to row right back; or row out, you see. Course things got better when you got the motor boats. Well, you really didn't want the sails then, but we always carried a big sail in fear if the engines gave out. Because we wasn't used to engines, you see, we had to learn all that.'

Sightings were taken at sea to locate spots where pots had been placed. The sightings were the lining up of objects on shore and were named, such as 'Two Chapels', in line with the ruined chapel in Hallsands and a disused one to the north-west along the road to Chillington. Others involved various man-made or natural objects. 'Peartree Point in Rough Rocks' was the sighting 'taken by Beesands': where Peartree Point south-west of Start Point lined up with the Rough Rocks 'behind' Start Point. There was also 'Eastland in Start Point' (the end of the land on the north-east tip of Start Point) and 'Eastland in Black Stone' (a rock in the sea south of Start Point). 'Deep Water Mark', marking the deepest water between the shore and Skerries Bank, was a line between Start Point and the first houses in Beesands.

Various fishing grounds were named and bounded between sightings: so, 'Start Ground' lay between 'Eastland in Start Point' and 'Eastland in Black Stone'. There was also 'The Rudd', 'Baltic Ground', 'Klondike', and 'High Market'. The latter two are 'Beesands names'. The characteristics of the bottom of the various grounds were recognized, some having 'heaving ground' where pots are moved by the tide. This, however, is not a problem for the modern large boats with their larger strings of pots. The Hallsands men fished west of Start Point. Most Beesands men fished seaward of the Skerries Bank. There is too much sand on the bank itself to allow crabbing and the pots would be buried.

Pots were hauled in ('pulled') by hand up to 1969 with only one or two pots in one location. The pots in use then were a bit wider than those in use after pots were no longer pulled by hand, but their funnels were the same size. Pots were afterwards hauled by use of bollards which ran off the engine; however, some boats had a separate two-stroke engine to run the bollard. With bollards, pots were first put out in strings of four and later six. Willow pots were too fragile to be stacked so they took up much room on deck, being placed on all available space. The older engines had no reverse or neutral and had to be shut off when hauling. They had to be started by hand fifty or sixty times a day.

The fishermen went out to haul pots an hour after high water and an hour after low water. The pots were stationary on the bottom and the tidal flow pulled the marker floats attached to the lines under water, so pots could not be located or hauled at other times. When the tide was at its highest it started to 'ease off'. When the tide was between high (flood) and low (ebb) it was dead still. There was less pull on the tide near the shore. Inside the 10 fathom line 'you are able to see the pots'; that is, they were not pulled under by the tide. When there was a 'swell' the fishermen let the waves 'assist them' in hauling. They gathered the rope in the trough of the wave and not in the swell making the pitch of the boat 'work for them'.

Buoys had to be small enough to go under water during the tidal pull or the pots would drift away, despite the fact that they were weighted to keep them from drifting. If pots were made so heavy as to keep them from floating away when attached to buoys large enough to keep them from being pulled under when the tide was running, they would be too heavy to haul up by hand. In a running tide the pots were not sufficiently buoyant to be lifted to the surface. The buoys came to the surface in the slack periods between the tides and the fishermen had to be there at the right time.

Working on the 'high water tide' the potters would be out an hour after high water as the flood tide would then be easing. This was the best tide to work, the 'true tide'. Sometimes they had to go out an hour after low water. With the 'low water tide' the flood water would start before the ebb finished. With the flood tide there was always a slack period but not with the ebb tide. The tides ease first closest to the shore and then further out as time goes on – the potters worked from the inside out. The flood tide flowed north; the ebb flowed south. With the ebb tide the crabbers had to be out quick enough at the shoreward pots first before the flood tide took them under. Further out they would wait for the tide to slack and the floats to come up. The ebb seemed to run longer than the flood in terms of keeping floats under water and the fishermen might have had to wait two hours if there was a spring tide. They liked to use the first tide in the morning because it was the calmest.

The crab pots used were of the 'ink-well' type as used in Cornwall.[14] In shape they resemble an upside-down basket with a flat bottom and a hole at the top through which the crabs enter and are removed. The pots were woven by the potters themselves out of willow branches from trees in groves growing on the land of local farmers. The farmers were paid for the use of the land by receiving fish or labour. Seine crews would collect and bring in willows together, but they would be woven for, and by, members of boat crews. Larger 'store pots' were also made and used to keep crabs after they had been caught.

There was a 'crab smack', a sail boat, that came from Southampton to pick up the crabs every week or two up to the First World War. It had a 'well' in it in which the crabs were kept alive. From Southampton the crabs were sent by rail to Billingsgate Market in London. From 1968 to the spring of 1974, when the traditional fishery was given up, the crabs were sold to the East Devon Shellfish Company which picked them up and paid 8d. per pound. They also

Mr Hutchings Senior at Beesands with a crab-pot made by himself from local willows (Dorothy Dix)

brought bait and deducted that from the amount paid. They would have stopped coming even if the Hallsands fishery had not stopped, because it had ceased at Beesands. Before 1968 crabs were taken by lorry to Beesands and the charge for hauling was 21d. per cwt.

Lobsters would be taken occasionally. The best lobstering was from February to March but they were also taken from June to the end of October. Pots were put out in 4 fathoms of water by rocks. The pots were of the ink-well type, made specifically for lobsters, but lobsters were sometimes caught in the crab pots.

A fisherman's wife described the daily activities from a domestic point of view:

'We got meals according to what time the fishermen came in. They got themselves toast and tea before going out early. If they got back at 9 a.m. they got a fried breakfast. They would usually be out again then. If they got back at 11 they got dinner. During the summer they might be at Torcross at 1.30 to 2 (to catch sand eels). It required two to six or seven hauls to get bait. They would have tea on the beach about 5. They would bait hooks for longlining on the beach. They shot their gear at about 7 to 8 when the tide was right. They got home by 9 or 10. They were up the next morning at 3 to 4 to haul gear. They got in about 7 to 8 and got a bit of breakfast. They did this two or three times a week in the summer. Other days were not so bad. They went to their crab pots every day. They had to pack fish also.'

About forty pots would be 'fished' in winter and approximately sixty in summer. Men of past generations would say that 'you'd put out the pots when you heard the cuckoo', about mid-May. Additional pots would be put out then and worn ones replaced with newly made ones. In winter there was no fishing when the sea was rough.

Up to about the Second World War fishermen helped on farms with the harvest which started in August and lasted about six weeks. Farmers also were helped by the fishermen from time to time in various other ways. In exchange for their labour the fishermen got the use of the willow beds from which the branches used for making the ink-well pots were taken.

Before the First World War, before the time of motor boats, the crabbers would wait up by the Start Point lighthouse after the morning's hauling (around 10 or 11 a.m) and the women would carry their lunches to them. Then they would work the next tide and be back home again by 3 or 4 p.m. Then they had to 'put up' potting for a day when they went for bait.

The crab pots themselves formed the subject of Dorothy Wright's study. In the latter part of her article, here omitted, modern methods of pot construction are described, with the use of man-made materials, the involvement of local firms and the exchange of ideas between French and English pot makers.

The wire crab-pot on the left and a willow pot on the right (Dorothy Dix)

Lobster and Crab Pots in the South Hams

On the last day of December 1963, I went to the village of Beesands which lies in the hundred of Colridge on the coast between Torcross and Start Point. It was at that time a small fishing community whose livelihood depended mainly upon the catching of crabs and lobsters in the area of the Skerries Bank and Start and Prawle Points. These crabbing grounds are reputed to be among the best in the British Isles and crabs have been caught from the Skerries weighing as much as 12 pounds.

Most people will still be familiar with the old lobster or crab pot, dome-shaped and made of willow rods or withies, though it belonged much more to the West Country, from Dorset westward, than it did to the east and north. Like so many of the world's fishtraps it is a non-return valve. One sees few willow pots today because they have been superseded by very different ones, but in the winter of 1963 many of the fishermen of Beesands were still harvesting their willows ready to make supplies of pots for the spring and summer fishing.

Materials

The willows were grown for this sole purpose in local beds or groves at Beeson and Hallsands. The grove in the Beeson area was in two parts but on the Tithe Map it appears as one.[15] It lay in the combe – Widdicombe – running due east and west and sheltered from the south-westerlies. The soil was red and rich, grass and corn growing to the north side and an orchard to the south. Both parts of the grove were surrounded by banks of earth and large stones 3 to 4 feet high. The two entrances were wired up and the bed was thick with brambles, weeds and ivy. The stools had obviously not been cut for two or three years, possibly more.

I learnt that the Beesands men had abandoned this little grove and were then sharing the Hallsands groves. These were much larger, running in an almost unbroken line from the crossroads below Batten and Greenstraight, between the road and the stream for approximately half a mile, in some places ten yards wide, in others much more. The acreage was hard to assess but it appeared to be greater in 1963 than in 1847 (the date of the Tithe Map) when it was rather over two acres. The beds were open and well kept and land was level. The crop looked good and most were green willows though there were a few stools of small bright red plants, *Salix purpurea*, probably crossed with *Salix viminalis* or *Salix triandra*. At the bottom of the combe is a large reed bed above the pebble ridge which tops the foreshore. This probably filters the salt spray which would otherwise sweep the willows in wild weather. But *Salix purpurea* in particular does not mind salt and the grove cannot be more than 250 yards from the sea at its lowest point. I was told that the Hallsands men have the willows nearest the sea and their boats.

A study of the Tithe Maps of Stokenham, Chivelstone, South Pool and East Portlemouth made in December 1975 showed the presence of many small willow groves near villages and farms,[16] nearly all under half an acre in area, which must have provided material for lobster-pots as well as for farm baskets traditionally made in the winter, or for repairing those bought from a basketmaker. There is evidence of small groves in the rest of Devon but nearly all have been grubbed up long ago and only the Tithe Map or a field name remembers them.

The fishermen of Beesands told me that they could not remember a time when the community did not have a withy bed, small wonder since the valley is called in Domesday 'Wodiacoma', the willow combe. Of late if there was a temporary shortage they used to buy 'Champion' willows from Stoke St Gregory near Taunton. This no doubt was the case when they returned in 1943 after the United States Invasion Army gave back the whole area after occupation in the Second World War, until the overgrown and neglected beds became productive once more.

I was told that in making pots a man tended to have his favourite colour of withy. He would say that the crabs prefer red or green or gold. (No withies are peeled.) Willows cross-fertilize so easily that there are, or have been in the past, dozens of kinds of basket willow, each with a name and sometimes a legend attached. The kind Beesands used for the standards, overheads and creasers, that is the longest rods in a pot, is 'Mailey Tops', probably 'Mealy Tops'. For the weaving they used 'Black Maul' or 'Greens' or 'Greys' or a short red willow I saw growing which might be a descendant of the famous extinct 'Dicky Meadows', so much revered by the makers of fine baskets in the late nineteenth century, first grown at Mawdesley,

Lancashire. If they had bought willows from upcountry it would be easy enough to grow a new kind by sticking a slip of a rod in the ground.

On this December day I saw bundles of fresh-cut willows being stacked against the sea wall. I was told by Mr Hutchings, one of the boat owners, that in the next fortnight everyone would be making pots and each house would have willows leaning against the walls, drying off. No basketmaker would use green willows like this because the work shrinks as they dry, but for pots this is good because as soon as the pot is submerged it swells again and becomes hard and heavy.

Making a willow pot

Mr Hutchings explained to me the special vocabulary used in making Beesands pots and though two strokes used in making baskets are used, i.e. pairing – a twist with two rods round the uprights,[17] and waling – a twist with three rods round the uprights going in front of two and behind one in sequence,[18] neither of these two words is used. It is possible that different sets of terms were used in many different places. I have only been able to find a few. But apparently most pots are made with the rings reverse-paired, while Beesands makes paired rings. Reverse-pairing[19] is the basket-maker's normal stroke for openwork.

Beesands calls the form on which a pot is made a mule. It is a disc of wood with a central hole which revolves on the top of a pole about 3 feet high, with strings attached near the base. The mule has a circle of holes drilled in it.

— 3 —
THE BRIXHAM TRAWLERS

Fishing enterprise forms only one of the strands in Brixham's long maritime history, but is the one which is inseparably linked with the name of the town. During the nineteenth, and the first decade of the twentieth century the red-sailed trawlers with their distinctive rig were familiar in many ports as they often landed their catches far from home. In Mr Straight's words, 'Brixham men were respected in all the fishing ports of the coast from Bristol to South Wales round to Hull'.

Percy Russell found evidence of trawling at Brixham as early as the fourteenth century while Michael Straight traced the origin of the (fully developed) industry to a date sometime after 1870. It is in fact possible to reconcile these widely diverging statements. A trawl net of some form seems to have been used at a very early date, but employment of a trawl held up by a wide beam and therefore allowing a larger catch came very much later. Percy Russell believed that this took place in the last quarter of the eighteenth century and that it was linked to the evolution of a suitable rig and hull form. (The rig allowed comparatively high speed, and the hull made it possible to handle the larger beam.) However, it was not until 1877 that the number of Brixham fishing vessels finally exceeded the number of commercial vessels registered there, according to research by J. E. Horsley.[1]

Payment of crews by shares and not by wages, and the distinctive form of the iron at the end of the trawl beam point to the development of the trawl, when it came, as independent of outside influence. Once established, the trawlers rapidly increased their range. They were wintering off Ramsgate by 1833 and permanent colonies of Brixham men were established at Hull by 1851 and at Grimsby seven years later. Westwards, Brixham men were established at Tenby and even in south-eastern parts of Ireland by 1863.

The Brixham crews had a reputation for opening up new fishing-grounds. The discovery of the 'Silver Pits', a rich ground south of the Dogger Bank, in about 1840 is attributed to them in some stories, although the claim is not uncontested. In more general terms it was certainly they who pioneered grounds only later exploited by steam trawlers from Grimsby or from Fleetwood.

The impact of the steam trawlers from the East Coast ports had by the 1890s robbed the Brixham vessels of their most lucrative fishery. However the Brixham fleet turned westward to intensify their operations in the Bristol Channel and Irish Sea.

The following passage written by Walter Garstang in 1903,[2] speaks in admiration of the resource and resilience of the Brixham men. It also shows that even in the greatest days of the smacks, fishing the home grounds formed a significant part of Brixham's involvement in the trade. The smaller vessels employed were nicknamed 'Mumble Bees' – a name evocative of South Wales, with which Brixham had known links. Alternatively, the term could surely be purely Devonian. Reference to 'Spion Kop', from a supposed resemblence of the cliffs on the Dorset side of Lyme Bay to hills made famous by the Boer War, firmly dates the time at which the account was written.

The Brixham Fishing-grounds and Fishery Statistics

There was a time, and that not many years ago, when the fishing boats of Brixham sailed round to the east coast of England and joined with the fleets of London, Lowestoft, Yarmouth and Grimsby in exploiting the fishing-grounds of the North Sea. This carries us back at least two generations, but we may turn to the doings of the men of Brixham at the present day.

Even a casual visitor to this port of South Devon would notice at once that the big boats are of two distinct types and sizes, the larger ones ketch-rigged, the smaller mostly with the cutter rig, and this would suggest differences in the size of gear employed and in the fishing-grounds visited by each. The large boats are over 50 tons burden, intentionally under-rigged, and able to go anywhere and stand any sea short of that raised by a hurricane. The trawl they use is of 45–47 foot beam. The small boats mostly run about 25 tons, and in unsettled weather cannot venture more than a few miles from land. Their trawl has only a 36–40 foot beam.

The large boats, generally called the 'smacks' or 'dandies', formerly journeyed every year to the North Sea, but some twelve years ago they were crowded out by the ever-increasing fleets of Lowestoft,

Mule class trawlers. These sailed out of Dartmouth, but a great many sailed out of Brixham (H. Winter Sharpe Esq.)

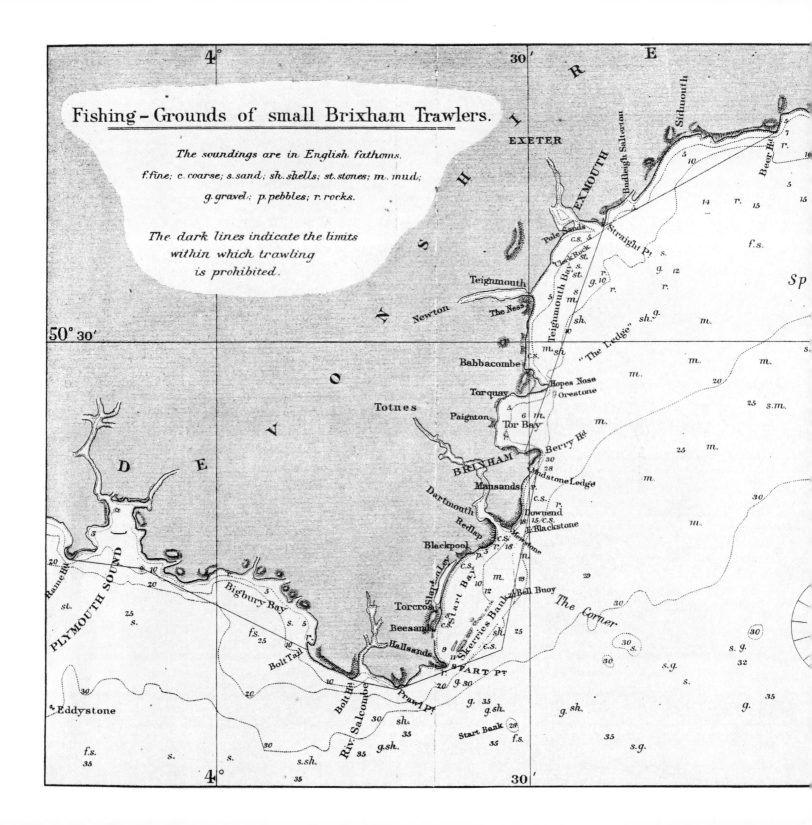

Fishing-Grounds of small Brixham Trawlers.

The soundings are in English fathoms.

f. fine; c. coarse; s. sand; sh. shells; st. stones; m. mud;

g. gravel; p. pebbles; r. rocks.

The dark lines indicate the limits
within which trawling
is prohibited.

Journ. Mar. Biol. Assoc. Vol. VI. N.º 4.

The Brixham Trawlers

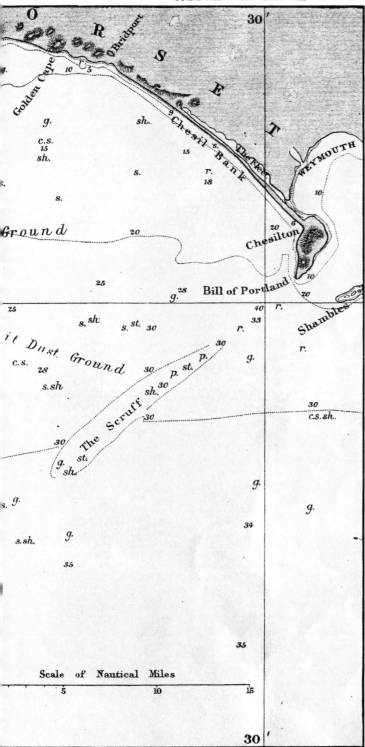

Yarmouth, and Grimsby. Some of the men remained at these ports, and have aided in making them great fishing centres, but the majority turned in the opposite direction, and as the English Channel was seemingly not rich enough to support all, they made their way into the Bristol Channel. There they discovered new and exceedingly rich trawling-grounds, and year by year they have continued to pass round Land's End in early spring, gradually extending their field of operations along the costs of North Cornwall, Wales, and Ireland as far north as the Irish Sea, and opening up new fishing centres, such as Milford and Dublin, wherever they went.

Since the majority of these boats are away from Brixham for the greater part of the year, and mostly land their fish at other ports, it is impossible to obtain even an approximate measure of the value of the grounds on which they fish. Some impression of their richness may, however, be obtained from the quantities of soles occasionally sent over to Brixham by rail from Padstow in North Cornwall:

During March	1902	12 700 pairs of soles.
During April	1902	17 400 pairs of soles
During May	1902	8300 pairs of soles

The ground on which these are caught, said to be very course and rough, is called by the fishermen 'ross'-ground on account of the hard masses of *Lepralia* and of *Alcyonium* on shells, which abound there. Plaice, turbot, and rays are also caught in considerable quantities, but the distinctive feature is undoubtedly the large supply of soles.

As the boats move further up the Bristol Channel and on to the Welsh grounds, their catches are quite lost to Brixham, which renders it impossible to give even a sample of what they obtain. According to all accounts, however, the characteristic of the fishing is still the great capture of soles.

Whilst the majority of the smacks spend the greater part of the year on the west coast, a varying number remain nearer home, and in the autumn all the boats are fishing in the English Channel. The grounds they work over extend from Portland to Land's End, usually between the 20- and 40-fathom lines. The nature of the grounds is practically the same throughout, and is of sand, shell, and gravel, with patches of stones and occasionally fine sand. As may be imagined, the catches consist largely of rays, red gurnards, and the prime fish – soles, turbot, etc. Sometimes the turbot seem to be exceedingly abundant, as during the past autumn, and in certain places, e.g. Mount's Bay, large quantities of plaice and soles are caught in their seasons. On the rough patches, off Start Point and off Portland, the liners ('Bolters') procure great hauls of conger, cod, ling, and rays. Since the smacks frequently land their catches at Plymouth, or at various ports in the south of Cornwall, it has been found impossible to give even an approximate measure of the value of the grounds in question. That these are rich and valuable there can

Plan of fishing-grounds off the South Devon coast annexed to Walter Garstang's report of 1903

27

be no doubt, for they support the Plymouth sailing trawlers all the year round as well as frequent steam trawlers from French and English ports. But the roving instinct of the Brixham fisherman, as well as his desire for greater gains, leads him to prefer the Bristol Channel.

We come lastly to the home grounds and the small trawlers. A few of the large smacks fish on these grounds occasionally in the intervals of coming from and going to the Bristol Channel; but they may be neglected for the present until we have discussed the fishing of the small boats. These number about seventy, and are known locally by the peculiar term 'Mumble Bees', said to be derived from a small fishing village called Mumbles, near Tenby in Wales. Some of the fishermen who went round to the Bristol Channel found at Mumbles this smaller type of boat, cutter-rigged and about 25 tons, and adopted it for the inshore fishing near Brixham. It follows that the Mumble Bees are a comparatively recent innovation, though it must not be supposed that there were no small trawlers at Brixham before their introduction. As a matter of fact, there was a smaller class of boat, under 5 tons and without a deck, which still persists at that port and other places round the coast, but they are for the most part employed in hooking or lining at the present time.

The fishing-grounds of the Mumble Bees lie within the area Start Point to Portland. If a line were drawn from Start Point six miles to the south-east, thence to the inner edge of the 'Scruff' and on to Portland, it would embrace the region beyond which the Mumble Bees seldom venture. The line would enclose about 700 square miles of sea, little more than half of which is worked by the trawlers. Rocks prevent trawling within the 15-fathom line from the Ore Stone off Torbay right to Portland, and there are several rocky patches off Downend, i.e. between Berry Head and Start Point. The trawlable area is thereby reduced to less than 400 square miles, and 70 square miles have been further cut off by the closure of the inshore grounds – that is to say, the proportion of the enclosed grounds to the outside trawlable area is about one-fifth.* Before the closure of the bays the outside trawling-grounds were more restricted, but since that time the fishermen have been driven by force of circumstances to trawl on grounds they had never before frequented.

The various parts of the trawling area are fairly well differentiated from one another by the bottom-soil, and are known to the fishermen by distinctive names. Along the northern portion, in 15–22 fathoms, lies the 'Spion Kop' ground, so called by the Brixham men from some fancied resemblance along the promontories along the coast to the famous battlefield in Natal. The soil is composed of medium to fine sand, with coarse patches here and there. *Pectens* (queens) and other shellfish are abundant, and the ground is liable to become very foul by sudden incursions of star-fishes, sea-urchins, and drift-weed.

How these can suddenly appear and as quickly disappear within a few days is one of the unsolved mysteries of the region.

The Brixham men did not trawl on this Spion Kop ground until three years ago |1900|, and visit it only during the Spring. At that season the plaice are returning to the inshore waters, and this is one of the main lines of the migration. The plaice are not large, and last year |1902| they were said to be smaller on the average than in previous years. Soles are also obtained there, as are whiting, dabs, and gurnards; but the mainstay of the fishing is the plaice.

To the south-east of the Spion Kop ground lies the 'Biscuit Dust' ground, 12 miles off Berry Head and running up to within 6 miles of Portland. It is so called from the bright golden yellow colour of the coarse sand and shells which compose its soil. Starting at about 27 fathoms, it extends out to 30 fathoms, where it merges into the 'Scruff'. The fish obtained here are plaice at the spawning time in early spring, soles, rays, and sometimes in the autumn considerable quantities of red mullet.

The Scruff is not a regular trawling-ground, its coarse soil and 'hummocky' nature being too dangerous, especially for the comparatively light materials of which the small trawlers' nets are made. The large smacks with their stronger nets of manilla might tow over it and at the eastern corner the longliners often procure large catches of ling and rays. At the western end of the Scruff, however, lies a favourite trawling-ground, especially in late Spring, when fine catches of whiting are often obtained.

Following along the line of the Scruff, towards Start Point, we come to the 'Corner', which in late Spring and Summer is the rendezvous of all the small trawlers. It lies across the 30-fathom line, 6–10 miles off Dartmouth Fairway with Prawle Point clear of Start Point. Fish are abundant there during the season, and include soles, lemon soles, a few turbot, plaice, dabs, whiting, gurnards, and rays; in fact, it is the richest ground within the area. The invertebrate fauna is also rich and distinct from that of the other grounds. The crabs *Polybius*, *Atelecyclus*,

Berry Head and Brixham (West Country Studies Library)

* The proportion is less in reality, because the crab pots on the Skerries Bank and the rocks closer inshore cut off one-third of Start Bay as a trawlable area. The proportion of trawlable area within the enclosed waters to that outside is therefore about one-sixth.

28

Corystes, and the heart-urchin *Echinocardium* are more plentiful here than anywhere else.

The central region of muddy ground has no particular name, but is well fished over at all seasons of the year for the sake of the ubiquitous whiting. Along the western margin of the area there are several well-known trawling-grounds, e.g. 'New Ridge', off Downend, and the 'Hitches', off Berry Head, which really form part of the central region, and require no special mention.

Michael Straight[3] wrote a long and highly valuable study of the Brixham fishing industry and of its history in 1935. Any comment on this classic exposition of the rise and fall of an industry would be impertinent except perhaps to mention that it forms only a part of the original.

The History of the Decline

The history of the Brixham fishing industry begins some time after 1870. At that time the schooners which the Brixham merchants ran to Newfoundland and the Canary Isles were gradually being superseded by the new steamboats. The merchants searching for other channels of investment for their money, established the new fishing industry and became its original mortgagees. Before the tradition was established at Brixham, the skippers were given trials and kept if they were successful. The industry was built up on the apprentices which came from workhouses, orphanages and training ships. The large trawlers probably carried two apprentices – one as cook and one as third hand. Some took as many as three. The apprentices took no

Certificate of Competence as Second Hand granted to W.J. Quick in 1896. Quick had been an apprentice on the Ocean Ranger of Brixham in 1887 (West Devon Record Office)

Above:
Western Cliffs, Sidmouth, with fishermen, cottages and drying nets. Painted by the Rev. John Swete, 3 March 1795. (Devon Record Office)

Left:
The mouth of the River Otter in 1849 as seen by Peter Orlando Hutchinson. The capstan was for drawing boats up the beach (West Country Studies Library)

money wage but lived on the owner of the boat, who paid for their keep and gave them 2s. a week pocket money. The third hand also took 5s. a week stock-a-bait. Though the boat's earnings were still divided into eight shares, three-quarters of a share being nominally allotted to the upkeep of an apprentice, the owner, if he were also skipper of the boat, took its total earnings. In the years before the First World War there were about 150 apprentices in Brixham. They served two to three years as cook, becoming third hand at seventeen or so, then at nineteen they took their second hand certificate, and finally their skipper's certificate. Many got this at the age of twenty-one and there were consequently a great many young skippers in Brixham, as well as a continual flow of men from twelve years and upwards. The eldest man in a typical boat in pre-war years would not be much over thirty, the skipper might be twenty-four, and few skippers were over forty. Most of them were young skipper owners, in debt and anxious to earn back their money. The mate was the skipper's right-hand-man and as eager as the skipper himself. The apprentices were barely more than slaves and had no say in the boat's working. Consequently the fleet might be in Brixham for only two months in the year, fishing for the main part in the Bristol Channel.

Altogether, there were 213 trawlers registered in the books of the Mutual Insurance Society in 1910. This included the big trawlers, the mules, and the Mumble Bees, which fished inshore with longlines and which were rapidly dying out. Some of the boats naturally failed to pay. Some which fished the English Channel lost a great deal of gear, even before the war. On the whole, however, the industry was flourishing. The boats were up to date and the men were young and keen. The town of Brixham prospered from their success. The women knitted underwear for the apprentices and wove the nets. The older men went out in the other subsidiary industries such as sail making. One hundred and fifty men worked in the yards of the three shipwrights; seven firms make 288 pairs of sea-boots in a year, and nine out of ten of the young men of Brixham went to sea. Brixham men regarded themselves as a cut above the neighbouring fishermen in ports such as Plymouth (where the Brixham merchants now get their fish), and Brixham men were respected in all the Bristol Channel ports (which now dwarf Brixham in their landings). They regard themselves as the pioneers of the industry and the explorers of the untouched fishing grounds in the Bristol Channel and the Scilly Isles.

But the Brixham men were also the pick of the R.N.R. When the war broke out the fleet was summoned home, and from all directions they converged at Brixham. The Government took two hundred or so of the young men and put them in responsible positions in minesweepers and so on, guarding the Orkneys and Scapa Flow, while Scotchmen were brought to Brixham. These skipper-owners were forced to sell their boats, and so were some others, owing to the lack of men for crews. The high price of fish, however, caused the boats to be bought, and later their value rose considerably.

Shortly afterwards, the Government diverted the convoys through the fishing-grounds, and this attracted the submarines. Before the war the fishing boats (not including the gear) were insured with a local mutual insurance society. When a boat was lost, the loss was paid in 'averages' called up from the total fleet insured with the society, the amount being a fixed percentage of the insurable value of each individual boat. Under this scheme the owners had to pay for all losses. These amounted to £20 000 on the first twenty boats sunk by submarines. At one point three boats were lost in a single week owing to submarine action and the smack owners received calls of as much as £100 with a certain definite time in which to pay. The Government at this time was strongly urging the trawlers to take every possible risk in order to supply the country with food. Soon after it established a new insurance fund, but refused to insure the boats at more than their pre-war value, despite the fact that the value of the boats had risen enormously after the outbreak of war. These inflated values remained after the war, and even those men who had received compensation for the loss of their trawlers found that it would not go half way towards the price of another similar ship. The high prices of fish, however, enabled some owners to make large profits. Despite government regulation of prices, the total value of fish landed in Brixham in 1918 reached £296 602, well over three times the value of an equivalent catch in 1910-14, despite the fact that the sizes of the war-time catches were unparalleled in Brixham's history. Brixham at this time was fished by Belgian refugees among other people; the apprentices soon disappeared.

When the war was over the heroes returned to find that of the 193 boats that they had left, 86 remained. The prices of the trawlers that remained were completely prohibitive and there were few skippers' berths open to them. But the sea was their only calling, and being unable to resettle themselves, those that had any backbone left for the younger ports like Milford and Fleetwood, taking Brixham's life-blood with them and building up the fleets that have now left Brixham far behind in size and in methods.

A few remained and one well-known local fisherman is a typical example of these. Before the war, as a boy, he tried to get into the navy, but failed on account of his teeth. He came home and told his father, who said, 'Then you can only go trawling'. He started at eleven – leaving his father, to go and live as an apprentice in the house of his master. By the age of twenty-one he had passed his skipper's test and soon after, having saved £160, he applied to his uncle to lend him £580. With this and the credit from the tradesmen, he fitted out a boat, applied to Gloucester workhouse and a London reformatory school for two boys, and set out. Being young, he fished keenly – once, in 1912, setting out for the Bristol Channel in November and leaving the boat in Milford while he came home by train for Christmas. At the outbreak of war he was forced to return, however, and left for London without even landing his catch. Soon after he was forced to sell his boat.

The boat had cost him £1300 to put to sea. When the war was over, he returned, determined to get back into fishing as quickly as possible. He went to his builder and was unable to get a boat.

Eventually after months of waiting, he found an antique trawler in need of a new boiler and in general on its last legs, for £1000. Despite the ridiculous price, however, he decided to take it on. He went again to his uncle for a loan, and found that his uncle, like all the other local mortgagees, had tied up his money in 5 per cent war loan. The uncle, however, unselfishly sold out and re-lent his nephew the money. Despite the higher prices, however, the fisherman was unable to make the boat do anything more than barely clear itself. He sold it out again, having worked it for only a year, and retired.

Some of the younger men, however, egged on by the local tradesmen and the fish prices, and with some of the pre-war optimism still left in them, decided to build new boats and start again. As the fisherman says – it was their calling – there were no old boats left for them and either they had to leave Brixham or restart. So they put on a brave face and ordered new boats. Twenty were built between 1922 and 1927. The best was called the *Revive*, but most of them were a hopeless proposition from the first. The young owner-skippers had not realized that the capital cost of building had nearly doubled and that the enormous debts they would start with would cripple them from the beginning. By 1927 prices were falling – fish that was worth £91 000 in 1925 sold for £72 000 in 1927 – and by 1927 it was realized that the trawlers could never pay in the way that they had paid before the war. At that time too the Belgians, helped by an appreciative government and a low rate of interest, were beginning to profit by what they had learnt and the French were following suit. The young men were going and the apprentices had gone. From then on the fleet quickly declined in numbers.

In 1910 there were 213 boats registered in the society, with a capital value of £104 750. In 1913, owing to a decline in the number of Mumble Bees which were registered with the society, the total number fell to 193. (This fall, however, was compensated for by the growth in the number of motor boats, which were not registered.) In 1920 the number had fallen to eighty-six with a capital value of £38 050. By 1925, with twenty additions to the fleet in the large class, the number had risen to ninety with a capital value of £63 795. In 1930, however, the number was only fifty-eight and the capital value £39 720. Finally, in 1935, the number is only twenty-six and the capital value £23 000. The capital value here is, of course, the insured value, the present market value of the boats is actually far less.

Briefly then, the history of the industry can be divided into four periods. The period of prosperity up to 1914, the period of disaster during the First World War, the period of apparent revival from 1920 to 1927, and the period of gradual collapse from 1927 on.

Sadly, this collapse accelerated and by 1939 only six of the big so-called smacks remained.

This last passage, describing the trawl net, is taken from an official guide to Brixham Harbour printed during the 1960s. It is of interest as giving a description of the state of affairs at Brixham before the 'mackerel boom' of the 1970s. By 1974 the seven trawlers mentioned here had grown to number fifty-six and a new quay with facilities including a freezing plant had been built. By 1982

Brixham had risen once again to become Devon's premier fishing port if the value of catches was taken as the criterion.

The Trawl Net

Although the fisheries of Brixham achieved a high status in early times, it was the trawl which carried them to the top. We cannot tell when the trawl first arrived in Brixham. As mentioned elsewhere, it may have come with the Huguenots in the sixteenth century or it may have been here already. The principle was not new – it was known to the Romans in the shape of oyster dredges, and an instrument called a 'wondrychoun', very similar to a beam trawl, was the subject of a petition in Parliament in 1376. John Leland reported that, in about 1525, fishermen were repeatedly bringing up objects from the floor of Torbay 'yn theyre nettes', and as this is most easily done with a trawl and certainly not with the seine, one is left with the idea that perhaps the trawl was then in use. In the following century fresh soles were available in Exeter market at 1s. a pair, again pointing to the use of the trawl.

Basically the beam trawl is a large bag, the open end of which is attached at one side to a wooden beam – in this case the side becomes the top, and the ends of the beam are raised off the seabed by iron runners or 'heads'. The whole thing is then hauled along by a boat. The bottom of the bag is formed into a pocket and the end of this is tied up with a light rope. This is the 'cod' end. When the net is hauled aboard the cod end is swung over the deck, the rope untied and the catch drops out into the fish-pounds on the deck.

Until the mid-eighteenth century, the beams were quite short, and the trawl could be stowed across the square stern of the trawlers, but as vessels grew more powerful and beams longer it became necessary to work and stow the net on one side, the port side. In the last days of the sailing trawlers at Brixham the customary beam length went up to about 48 feet, although it was greater on occasions.

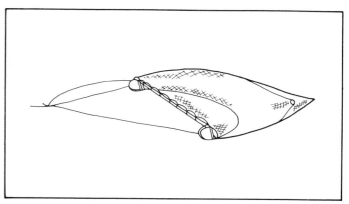

Beam Trawl

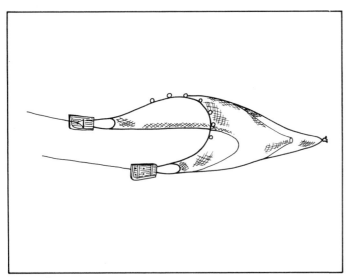

Otter Trawl

The beam trawl has long since been replaced by the otter trawl. This was due to the introduction of steam, which provided the constant speed required to prevent the otter boards from dropping flat on the seabed. It was tried with sailing smacks several times and produced good catches, but when it dropped flat as the wind eased, the whole net had to be hauled straight up from the bottom and shot all over again.

The otter trawl is held open sideways by the otter boards which operate rather like a kite but with water pressure, and floats hold up the headrope. Both these functions were served by the heavy beam and trawl heads in the older net. With no beam to stow, a very much larger net can be carried, giving correspondingly larger catches. Among the older men who have used both types at Brixham there are some who prefer the beam trawl, although it is no longer used. It is reputed to be far easier to handle once the beam is in, and, if the net should find an obstruction on the bottom, there is a better chance of breaking it clear with a beam – the otter trawl wraps itself lovingly round obstructions and often has to be cut away.

Although there are seven larger deep-water trawlers at Brixham now, most of the work is inshore, for which the otter trawl is not such a complicated affair. Only seven or eight floats are used on the headrope and it is altogether much smaller than the deep-sea version.

A more recent development of this type of net is the mid-water trawl. This is gradually coming into use locally for the sprat fishing season. Sprat fishing has become one of our more important seasonal fisheries in which most of the inshore boats participate. The mid-water trawl is worked between two boats, and it can be towed at the depth at which the fish are believed to be. So far the net has not proved an unqualified success, but this may be partly due to the fact that handling is not easy and needs a good deal of practice. Once it is mastered it may prove a most useful net.

Inshore boats also engage in crab and lobster fishing, and a few work the scallop beds. These beds are among the three main beds in Great Britain, but during the season the prices are so low that scalloping is not worth while, and the beds are therefore very little worked. Moral: eat more scallops – Brixham scallops.

There are other fish caught locally for which either there is no demand, or the market has not been fully exploited. Anchovies are sometimes caught but owing to lack of demand they are seldom landed. Whitebait, known in Devon as 'brit', abounds off the Devon coast in great shoals during the summer, yet no attempt is made to market this delicacy. There is still room for development at Brixham.

Modern electronic aids to the fisherman have done much to ease his task. Larger vessels carry radio telephones and direction-finding apparatus, and also the Decca Navigator. One or two of the smaller boats are taking up the Navigator, but it has not received universal acclaim among them. This is no reflection upon its efficiency whatever – it is ideal for an area where the fishing grounds are littered with the wrecks of two world wars and other obstructions. But the Navigator cannot be bought outright, only rented, and the rental charges are so high that the crew's income suffers considerably. Where it has been adopted, it has been in the hope that the reduction in damage to gear will offset it. By interchange of the information obtained with this instrument the fishermen have built up charts of the obstructions. A glance at one of these charts makes one wonder how any trawler could sail through without losing its gear. The fisheries have come a long way since the early North Sea trips without charts or instruments.

The Echo Sounder, in the version developed for fishing, is another great aid. By its use the fisherman can tell when he is over a shoal of fish and at what depth they are to be found. This saves a great deal of time and unnecessary work.

Brixham, in its long history as a fishing port, has seen many changes. Most of the better known methods of fishing have been used here at one time or another, from hooking to the modern mid-water trawl. Like an aged parent, her position in the fishing world is now well down the scale, but Brixham lives on still leading the fisheries of Devon. No doubt the future will see further developments in gear and methods, and it may yet become an important centre again. Long-term investment in new schemes, with parallel developments in vessels and harbour facilities, could bring fresh life to the industry. Sprats are a major industry, yet we still have no cannery, nor indeed a deep-freeze plant. Development in fish 'farming' will not be long in coming, and Brixham is ideally situated to take part in this. The research people tell us that there are tuna in the Atlantic off the south-west coasts, and that only the fringes of the great pilchard shoals are fished. It would seem that there is still plenty of scope for our fisheries, and the industry could yet provide the employment ashore that our growing population needs.

4

THE EXE AND TEIGN ESTUARIES
CREATURES GREAT AND SMALL

For different reasons both whaling and the eating of the lowly oyster are out of favour. In the eighteenth century the Exe estuary witnessed a short-lived, indeed fortuitous, link between the two. As will be seen, activity on the Exe sand- and mudbanks in gathering of oysters was matched for a period of thirty years or so by the intermittent visits of whalers and the boiling-down of blubber.

In the eighteenth century trade rivalry with Holland induced the English to pass legislation offering a bounty (subsidy) on all whaling voyages undertaken by their own seamen and merchants. As the following article by Conrad Dixon explains, it was this that made possible the use of so unpromising a base as the Exe estuary. The centre of operations was Parsonage Stile, the small bay to the north of Lympstone village which was even further reduced in 1861 when the Exmouth branch railway was built across it.

The Exeter Whale Fishery Company
1754-1787

Man's large-scale commercial pursuit of the Greenland Right Whale[1] dates from about 1610 when the Spitzbergen fishery was beginning to yield diminishing returns, and during the remainder of the seventeenth century whaling on the eastern coasts of Greenland was dominated by the Dutch. In 1719 their ships penetrated the Davis Straits and were soon bringing home rich catches of bone and blubber to the ports of the Zuider Zee. British whaling was in decline, but the revival of governmental and private interest in the trade owed much to the tireless canvassing of Henry Elking,[2] who persuaded the South Seas Company to fit out a fleet of a dozen whalers in 1725. The experiment was a disaster – principally because the crews were on regular wages and had no incentives by way of bonus or share in the catch – and after a loss of £9000 during the 1730 season the South Seas Company reduced its whaling involvement substantially. Elking had preached patriotism and profit, but the Whigs in Parliament had come to appreciate that the only way to break the Dutch near-monopoly of whale products was to subsidize whaling ventures, and in 1732 a bounty of 20s. a ton for vessels in the trade of over 200 tons burden was announced – a bounty payable, of course, after a whaling voyage had been completed.

The initial commercial response was cautious, but when the bounty was doubled to 40s. a ton in 1749 there was an immediate reaction, with merchants in London, Aberdeen, Hull, Leith, Peterhead, Dundee, Whitby, Lynn, Newcastle and Liverpool hastening to acquire whaling vessels. Their example was followed by other entrepreneurs in Greenock, Scarborough, Ipswich, Grangemouth, Bo'ness, Whitehaven, Dunbar, Glasgow, Montrose and Queensferry. Looking at this list of northern and eastern seaports one can see the logic behind a switch of resources to whaling – the geographical advantages, the long experience of the trade in many of these ports, the availability of experienced crews, marketing expertise and the knowledge that basic costs could be covered by the bounty. The port of Exeter, on the other hand, seems a less suitable base for exploiting Arctic waters. Its trade was traditionally orientated to the south and west,[3] it had no previous experience of whaling, no trained personnel, no marketing expertise and the port was difficult of access and with few facilities.[4] Nevertheless, in 1754, a group of thirty-two Exeter merchants came together to subscribe a total of £5125 to found the Exeter Whale Fishery Company with the object of engaging in the Greeland trade.

The accounts of the company covering the period from 17 October 1754 to 30 October 1759 survive, and are the chief source of our knowledge.[5] A 58-page ledger kept by Thomas Stokes, clerk to the company, tells us that the three individuals involved in day-to-day management decisions were Matthew Lee, a leading Exeter merchant who held the post of treasurer, Captain Thomas Colman, ship's husband, and Thomas Stokes. Matthew Lee was a shareholder and received no salary; Captain Colman, also a shareholder, was paid £15 a year and received three guineas a year for cellaring company stores, while Thomas Stokes received £16 a year for keeping the ledger, arranging meetings of shareholders, paying the crews, calculating bonuses and putting advertisements regarding oil, bone and fins for sale in the *General Evening Post*, the *Exeter Flying Post* and the *Daily Advertiser*. Colman, Lee and Stokes were present at all company meetings, which took place either at Swales Coffee House or the Salutation Inn, East Gate, Exeter, when, as is often the case today, the shareholders were plentiful in bad times and absent when things were going well.[6]

The first act of the new company was to acquire a ship, and Worthington Brice, a Topsham ship-builder, went off to London to buy a second-hand vessel suitable for Arctic whaling. He paid £2150 for a 346-ton ship later registered as the *Exeter*, and it was fitted out on the mudflats at Lympstone where the Newfoundland 'bankers' wintered,[7] being hauled off into deep water and anchored in the Bight off Exmouth in the spring of 1755. The ship went alone to the Greenland fishery in 1755-8, but in 1759 sailed in company with the 175-ton *Worthy Shepherd*, which was lost in the ice of the Davis Straits. The *Exeter* had a reasonably long life for a vessel in a hazardous trade, and although many times damaged by ice and taken by the French, and re-taken in 1760, she was still afloat in 1783.[8] Generally, *Exeter* left in April of each year and returned in August or September with her cargo. The profitability of the enterprise as revealed by the ledger is summarized in the following four tables, two giving the physical product in quantity and cash terms, one showing mean prices obtained for bone and oil and one the return on investment for a typical shareholder.[9]

It can be seen from Table 1 that the product in the 'good' years of 1755, 1756 and 1758 was fairly consistent, some five or six whales a season,[10] while Table 2 shows that prices fell slightly in 1756 but rose sharply in 1758, probably because of shortages attributable to the effects of the Seven Years War. The poor results in 1757 were due to an attack on the *Exeter* by a French privateer which caused her to abandon fishing for the season, while the loss of the *Worthy Shepherd* in the ice in 1759 meant that *Exeter* had to break off to rescue the survivors and salvage what she could from the wreck. The ledger contains the following melancholy entries in relation to the casualties of the action with the French privateer:

21-9-57   To pd, for a Coffin for Buyring Ben. Courtenay who was Kill'd Defending the Ship . . 19/6
          To pd. for a Coach to carry the Wounded men to Hospital . . 5/−

Subsequently the *Exeter* fitted a new mainmast, shipped extra guns and applied for a letter of marque.

Tables 3 and 4 highlight the importance of the bounty. In the 'good' years it amounted to over 22 per cent of the product in cash terms and in 'bad' years it provided over 90 per cent of the product. It supplied 55 per cent of the dividends drawn by the shareholders, and puts the Exeter Whale Fishery Company firmly into the category of a

Table 1

Product – Quantity				
Year	Voyage	Whales Taken	Bone	Oil
1755	1	6	57 cwt	64 tuns
1756	2	not known	48 cwt	69 tuns
1757	3	not known	--------	2½ hogsheads
1758	4	not known	55 cwt	55½ tuns
1759	5	not known	--------	--------------------

Table 2

Mean Prices		
Year	Bone (per cwt)	Oil (per tun)
	£ s d	£ s d
1755	14 9 0	18 2 6
1756	13 0 0	17 13 10
1758	18 15 0	25 0 0

Table 3

Product – Cash					
Year	Voyage	Bounty*	Oil	Bone	Total
		£ s d	£ s d		£ s d
1755	1	693 3 6	1111 0 3	883 6 2	2687 9 11
1756	2	693 3 6	1173 1 6	732 13 0	2598 18 0
1757	3	693 3 6	14 5 0	---------------	707 8 6
1758	4	693 3 6	1360 0 6	992 9 6	3045 13 11
1759	5	686 0 0	(53 8 1**)		739 8 1

* Bounty paid, less insurance.
** No bone or oil obtained in 1759, but this sum from sale of guns, surplus stores and wreckage.

Table 4

Return of an investment of £125			
Voyage	Date of Dividend	Amount	Return
		£ s d	
1	22–01–56	25 0 0	20%
2	17–09–56	25 0 0	20%
3	17–09–57	12 10 0	10%
4	undated	31 5 0	25%
-	undated	37 10 0	30%
5	30–10–59	21 12 1	17¼%

Note: A mean return of 24.45% annually over this period of five years.

Voyage 1st

1754				£		
October	19	To Cash paid Mr Brice for purchase of a Ship In London		2150	"	"
		To Do paid Mr Davey for Insurance of £ 1150 on Do	1	11	14	6
		To Do . . . Mr Neyle for Do . . . 1100	2	11	4	6
		To Do paid Capt: Hornsby for bringing the Vessel from London & other Services		21	"	"
		To Do paid Mr Fozer for Books and Paper	3	1	9	6
		To Do . . . Mrs Sarah Newman for 64 Iron bound Cashs	4	64	4	"
		To Do paid the fund for an Application to Parliament		10	10	"
Decr	13	To Mr Saml Follett for . . . Iron Hoops	5	71	1	11
1755 Febr	14	To . . . Richd Cross for 29 . 1 . 21 Pork at 13 . 4 ⅌C	6	34	6	6
	19	To . . . Jno Painter for Cashs & Coals	7	60	4	"
	21	To Passage of 7 Men from London	8	5	5	"
	25	To John Bartram for 62 . 0 . 24 Beef at 17 ⅌C	9	52	17	6
	28	To Wm Hillman & Son for 1 . C . 80 Pipe staves	10	50	"	"
		To Mr Worthy Brice in Part	11	20	"	"
		To Registering the Ship		"	10	6
March	26	To 24 Mushetts Cartouches &c	12	15	6	"
April	17	To Paid . . . for Insurance of £2500 at 6 ⅌C	13	150	"	"
		To Paid . . . for Do . . . of £1600 at 8 ⅌C	13	128	"	"
		To Paid for 3 Policy's	1	"	13	6
	18	To pd Mr Savage for Lights & Ramsgate duty for the Vessel from London & to Greenland	14	14	14	6
		To pd Mr Geo: Webber the Tinman for Kettles & Lamps &c	15	6	1	"

The opening 'Debtor' page of the Exeter Whale Fishery Company's ledger. Business was commenced with the purchase of a ship in London for £2150
(Devon Record Office - Exeter City Archives)

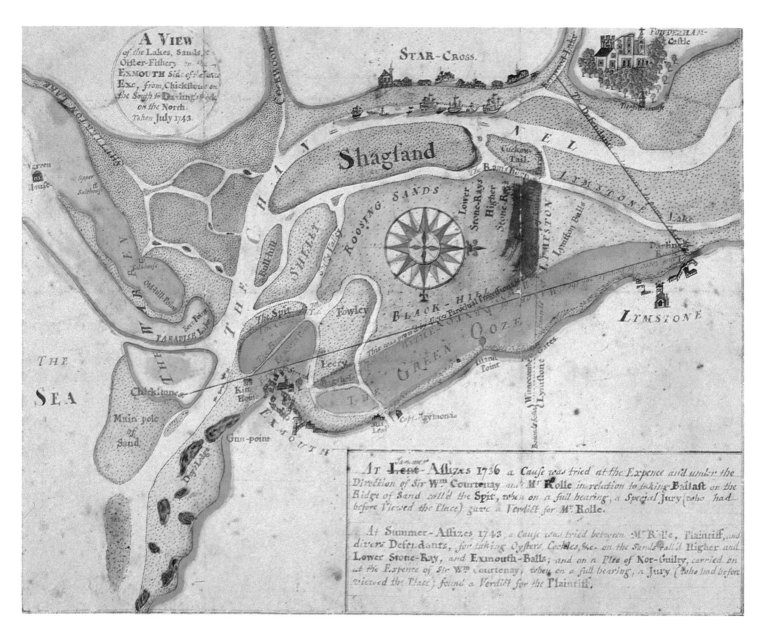

Above:
The Exe Estuary as it was in 1743 showing the 'Green Ooze' (Clinton Devon Estates)

Right:
Plan of Worthington Brice's Plot at Parsonage Style, Lympstone, in the late eighteenth century. Behind the quay and row of storage cellars on the waterfront are shown two buildings, one a smithy, the other, larger one containing a whale oil furnace (J.D. Meyrick Esq)

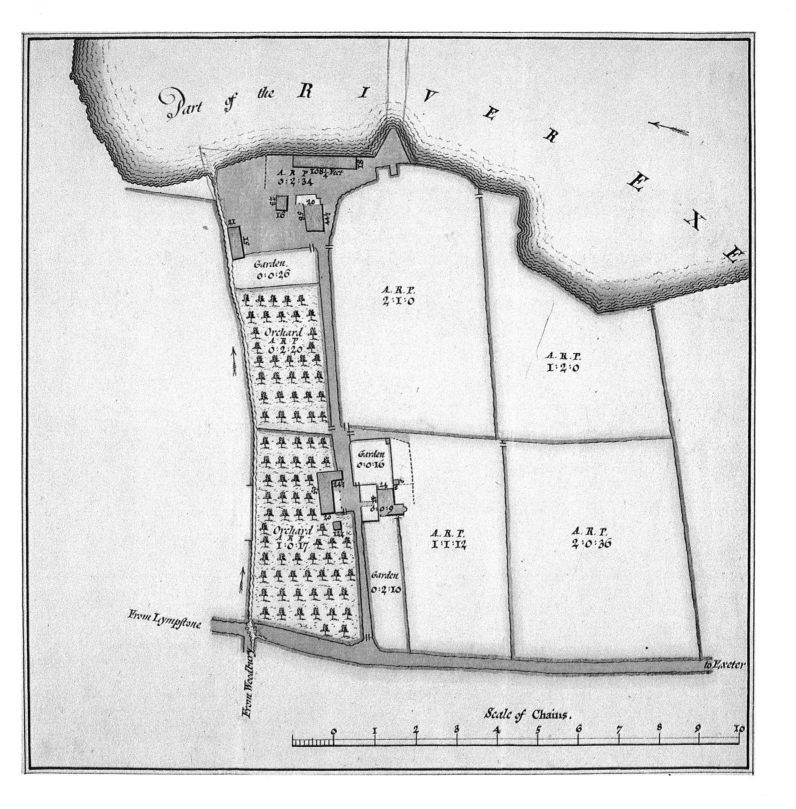

Part of the R I V E R E X E

A R P 108¼ Feet
0:2:34

Garden.
0:0:26

Orchard
A R P
0:2:20

A. R. P.
2:1:0

A. R. P.
1:2:0

Garden
0:0:16

0:0:9

Orchard
R
1:0:17

Garden
0:2:10

A. R. P.
1:1:12

A. R. P.
2:0:36

From Lympstone

From Woodbury

to Exeter

Scale of Chains.

0   1   2   3   4   5   6   7   8   9   10

Table 5

Bounty Paid on Whaling Tonnage[17]			
Year	sum	Year	Sum
1749	£1365	1755	£46 634
1750	£10 507	1756	£42 103
1751	£16 530	1757	£34 450
1752	£17 231	1758	£27 006
1753	£27 695	1759	£19 273
1754	£31 328	1760	£13 358

formally-supported unit of enterprise. One writer[11] has calculated that by 1769 the British government had paid out £600 000 to break the Dutch dominance of whaling, and when in 1777 the bounty was reduced to 30s. a ton, the number of whaling ships dropped by two-thirds. Alarmed lest the Dutch should recapture the industry, Parliament restored the bounty to 40s. a ton, but as the Dutch continued to contract their whaling fleets the bounty was brought down to 30s. in 1787 and 20s, in 1795.[12] The Exeter merchants were well informed about these developments; the last advertisements for whaling products appeared in the *Exeter Flying Post* in 1779, and the company ceased trading around 1787 when the *Lympstone* and the *Alcyone* made the last voyage from the Exe to Arctic waters.

The *Exeter* was of average size for the trade, but seems to have had smaller crew than was customary.[13] No full crew list survives, but by inference she had a crew of thirty made up as follows:

Captain
2 mates
'Speeksneer'[14]
3 harpooners (one acted as gunner and one as 'Speeksneer's mate')
Boatswain
Carpenter
Cook
Cooper
12 seamen
3 'oilers' (flensers)
4 apprentices

The captains (Captain Shepherd in 1756, Captain Phillips in 1758 and Captain Hart in 1759) received a salary of £60 a year, plus 'oyl money' at 10s. a tun and 'whale money' of three guineas a whale. Thus, in the first year the captain received a total of £110.18s. The 'Speeksneer' or chief harpooner got a bonus of 6s. 4d. a tun of oil and the mates and harpooners 6s. a tun. The harpooner who acted as 'Speeksneer's mate' received 5s. 3d. 'cutting money' for working with a cutting spade on the back of the whale while the hands turned the

dead beast with ropes or chains to expose new areas of flesh. On the early voyages there was a predominance of Scots mates and harpooners, and the ledger mentions the payment of the coach fares from London for these officers, but later most recruiting was local, although the apprentices continued to travel from London and were fed, lodged and doctored ashore before joining the ship in the Exe. The Globe Hotel at Topsham[15] was the usual venue for signing articles and the accounts give an indication of the convivial nature of the proceedings with entries such as '. . . to the Harpooners to drink when they entered into Contracts . . . 5s.' and '. . . to the crew to drink the Owner's Health . . . £1.1s'.

Disciplinary problems were few, although two apprentices ran away in 1759, and the diet was well above average for a ship of the period. Pork, beef, mutton, biscuits, oatmeal and flour were shipped in quantity, while cheese, beer, pease pudding, potatoes, butter and sugar supplemented the basics. For the after guard there was wine and tea, the eggs of twelve hens and mustard and cress grown from seed. On the voyage *Exeter* loaded 136 gallons of brandy, but since it would have been well-nigh impossible for that amount to be consumed by even the thirstiest ship's officers in a four months' voyage, we can assume that much of the spirit was for trading purposes.

The Exeter Whale Fishery accounts shed some light on the commercial morality of the time with entries such as '. . . to fee the clerks for expediting the Licence . . . 10 6d.' and '. . . to expense at the Globe to Clear Impress'd Sailor . . . 1s. 8d.', showing that the machinery of officialdom required occasional oiling, while the conduct of the company treasurer, Matthew Lee, cannot be said to have been entirely honourable. As the chief officer of the company he could not very well sell company products openly to himself, and the company ledger shows no such transactions. However, his private books [16] tell a different story. In 1756 there is an entry '. . . by profit on Whale Oyl sent to Bilbao . . . £26. 19s. 10d', and in the following year he made ten guineas on a similar deal, both of which were, no doubt, the fruits of dealing in company products through nominees or intermediaries. The shareholders, too, must have been aware that they were getting over half their dividends from general taxation, for having laid out £5125 and received £6254.10s.5d. in dividends it cannot have escaped their notice that £3458.14s. of their return came from the bounty. To emphasize this point Table 5 gives the figures paid nationally in bounty, and one can see at a glance that the Exeter merchants came into whaling just before the peak year of 1755, while we know from other sources that they ceased whaling in 1787 – the very year that the bounty dropped permanently to 30s. a tun.

In view of all the foregoing should we conclude that the existence of a substantial subsidy was the chief reason for the formation and operation of the Exeter Whale Fishery Company? Some facts point to this counclusion: the small crew in relation to the size of vessel, the care taken to insure both the bounty and the vessel for more than it was worth, the entry into the whaling industry when bounty payments were near their national peak, the exit from it the moment the bounty dropped permanently below 40s. a tun and the fact that in the years for which we have detailed records the bounty provided 55 per cent of the profits. On the other hand the elements of patriotism and profit cannot be ignored. The writings of Henry Elking and others spurred entrepreneurs on to ship more goods in British bottoms and diminish Holland's entrepôt role, while at the local level the shareholders of the Exeter Whale Fishery Company voted, and paid for, an 'advice boat' to go to Greenland to warn all British shipping of the outbreak of the Seven Years War. The mid-eighteenth century saw a marked decline in Exeter's cloth trade, and in the subsequent diversification that followed a return of 11 per cent (dividend less its bounty element) from whaling was by no means contemptible. It would be wrong to regard the company as merely a hot-house flower quite unable to face the blasts of perfect competition, for in many respects the Exeter merchants were right to give up whaling after 1787. The Dutch had been ousted by the British, who went on to develop new fisheries in other oceans,[18] but the irony of the situation is that within fifty years the British were to be almost wholly displaced by the Americans, and whaling products ceased to make an important contribution to the national economy as alternative raw materials took the place of the oil and bone harvested with such difficulty from the grey waters of the Davis Straits.

Oysters and 'Muscles'

Literary references in Victorian times — one has only to think of 'The Walrus and the Carpenter' — show how the oyster was then thought of as a splendid food. Numerous references in records show that oysters were cultivated in the estuaries of the Fal, at Plymouth, and in the Teign and the Exe until the present century.

At low tide there lies between the rivers Exe and Clyst a mudbank known as 'Greenland'. It would be pleasant to think that this was a folk-memory of the whale trade. 'Go aground there', the saying might have run, 'and you might as well be in Greenland although in sight of home.'

A more likely origin is more prosaic. A map of the Exe 'Oister beds' disputed between Rolle and Courtenay in 1743 shows the 'Green Ooze' between Exmouth and Lympstone. Greenland is probably so named in such a context as this.

In October 1743 the unlucky Jonathan Brimble, water bailiff to Kenton, was fined £3. His offence was in 'suffering a north-country man to dredge oysters', within the manor (adjudged to include the western shores of the estuary). The north-country man had doubtless come with a coal ship from Durham or Northumberland with a cargo bound for Exeter. We are not told if he had let Brimble have some coal in exchange for going out to the oyster beds with him, for this is what had occurred.

On 23 September 1782 a bill for a mayoral banquet at Exeter included such incongruous items as the following:

Lobsters	4s.	6d.
Oisters	2s.	0d.
Paper		9d.
Wafers (for sticking paper together)		½d.
Cheese	2s.	0d.
Wax Candles	1s.	9d.
Cards	2s.	4d.
Cream		3d.

William Chapple, tireless and efficient agent of Sir William Courtenay and unfulfilled local historian of merit, was one who concerned himself with oyster production in the Exe estuary. As Steward of Kenton Manor Court he supervised proceedings on 12 June 1759 to regulate activities on the oyster beds and to improve them. Of particular concern to him was the invasion of the beds by mussels (consistently and comically spelled 'Muscles'). The proceedings included a 'Charge' (that is an inquiry or directive) followed by a 'Presentment' (or recommendation).

The Charge — 'You are also to enquire whether there be any Rent, Service, or Custom, due to the Lord of this Manor, and withheld from him; and (if any) what it is, from whom due, and for what lands, or otherwise, chargeable: And here I must not omit to take Notice of certain Rents or Payments which tho' not denied or withheld from the Lord, have been for some time neglected to be paid; I mean the accustomed Payment of *One shilling* yearly for the Privelege of having Oyster-Beds within this Harbour, the said sum being payable for every such Oyster-Bed. Nothing is hereby intended to deprive the Tenants or poor Inhabitants of this Benefit, but to *extend* and increase it; and at the same Time to preserve the Lord's Rights and Dues, which if not paid are presentable in this Court; and the Names of the Persons who ought to pay the same, that a Collection may be forthwith made thereof: And as the Harbour is now too much infested with Muscles which tend to the Destruction of the Oysters, the Dues so to be collected will be for the most Part applied to the clearing and removing the Muscles, and for the better Improvement of the Oyster-Fishery and the Advantage accruing from thence to the Inhabitants: and I can't help recommending to the Proprietors of the present Oyster-Beds *for their own Interest* to do *their* Parts towards removing those Muscles to preserve the said Oyster-Fishery; and therefore I also think such Poor Persons as choose to carry off Muscles should have them Gratis.'

The Presentment goes on to say that sixteen named occupiers of the oyster beds had neglected to pay their yearly shilling's rent, which they and others unknown ought to do. Chapple declares as Steward that Sir William Courtenay, baronet, will pay the expenses of clearing the beds now on condition that others do their part, and on the understanding that he does not give up his claim to the rent.

We are not told if the deserving poor appreciated the gift of 'Muscles' or how far this recommendation was acted upon.

Nevertheless, it is interesting to compare the attitude of the eighteenth-century administrator with that of the nineteenth-century merchant which follows it.

View on the River Teign (West Country Studies Library)

The Teign Oysters Beds

Oyster beds and shell fisheries were in the nineteenth century a feature of the Devon coastal scene; their popularity is indicated, for example, in a print issued about 1850 showing the 'Proposed Exe Bight Oyster Fishery and Pier'. However, in the 1860s Exeter Naturalists Club carried out experiments on oyster breeding at Lympstone because it was feared that although 'The West of England has been famous from time immemorial for its great abundance of oysters . . . the present system of dredging young oysters and the simultaneous abandonment of their feeding grounds by provincial oyster merchants, threatened to extirpate the oyster altogether'. John Horsley, writing in 1970, noted that the Teign, with its extensive mudflats, sustained cockle, mussel and oyster beds, but that as Teignmouth went early into the holiday trade shellfishing was always a secondary activity which by 1902 had diminished to a few cockles being raked in the river and a little seining for sand eels.[19]

H.J. Trump also has a brief reference in his history of Teignmouth to the shellfish beds: 'Fishing in the river offered little alternative employment since it was restricted by a Mr Knight and a Mr Baxter who . . . closed the oyster, mussel and winkle beds on the Shaldon side of the river to local people and enforced their rights by prosecution'. In 1880 it was estimated that one thousand million oysters were taken around Britain's coast, and Baxter's beds in the Manor of Bishopsteignton were to be increasingly exploited during the first half of that decade to increase their contribution to the national output.[20] It is these beds which are the concern of this article.

John George Baxter was a Billingsgate fish merchant and it will become clear that in the 1880s he began to increase his investment in the beds which he had leased since 1857 from the Reverend George Thomas Comyns, the Lord of the Manor of Bishopsteignton, and that the consequent stricter control over the beds was to clash with the perceived customary rights of the fishermen and women of Teignmouth.

After Comyns had granted the first lease to Baxter in 1857 further leases were granted in 1863 and 1883, the last lease being the one still running when the fishermen began their challenge. The area in dispute lay between the outflow of Broadmeadow Brook and the Shaldon Bridge.

The 1857 lease survives in the Comyns papers and permits Baxter to take 'all that salmon, oyster, mussel, periwinkle and cockle fishery in on or under so much . . . of the River Teign within the manor of Bishopsteignton', and 'to use . . . all legal ways and means for the protection and increase and preservation of the same': There was positive advice in the lease that only those employed by Baxter should be permitted to take the shellfish and an instruction to 'proceed against . . . and bring to Justice all and every person . . . found trespassing on or otherwise destroying or injuring . . . the beds . . .'.[21]

While the beds were slackly managed conflict was less likely, but there is evidence that in the 1880s Baxter increased his investment in the Teign. According to Edward Rice, who was Baxter's Teignmouth agent, 'some thousands of oysters were scattered and 15–20 tons of periwinkles laid down for breeding purposes'. In 1882, £169 was spent in building up the mussel beds and £247 in lifting them the following year. A further £240 was spent in 1884 to establish new mussels, which were still breeding in 1887. Rice also reckoned that between 1884 and 1887 a further £290 was spent on the beds. Baxter's London manager also had laid down in 1884 some £300–£400 of oysters.[22] Clearly there was scope for conflict between the desire to protect this investment and the fishermen's traditional activities in the tidal waters of the Teign.

At first the fishermen tried to secure the support of those in authority, the Teignbridge magistrates and the Board of Conservators for the Teign. C.H. Collings and F. Banbury laid a petition before the Teignmouth bench, in March 1885 to 'respectfully request your chairman to convene a public meeting in order to ascertain and uphold the ancient rights of the fishermen of the port of Teignmouth to fish at all legal times in the river and estuary of the Teign, which rights we have just reason to consider are at present unjustly usurped to the detriment of the general public of the Town' and so 'cause great suffering to the fishermen and those dependent upon

them'. The bench declined to give the lead in calling a meeting but favoured the idea of a meeting being called to support the rights of the town. When the Teign Conservators met at Newton Abbot that same month a fishermen's representative protested about Baxter placing notices prohibiting fishing in areas of the Teign which the fishermen considered public waters. However, the Board heard the advice of Lord Clifford's agent, Mr Knight, and decided it had no jurisdiction in this case.[23]

At this point in the dispute the *Western Times* considered there was a general 'impression that no one can lay claim to the beds over which the tide flows' and that 'the question of right will have to be tested, but unfortunately law proceedings are costly, and as most of the previous cases have been brought against poor people, the question has not been properly fought'.[24] Having failed to gain support from established authority the fishermen resorted to direct action by trespassing in the beds in November of that year. This alarmed the Teignmouth correspondent of the *Western Times*, who was to be proved correct in asserting that the county court was unlikely to upset Baxter's title and thought 'It was a great pity our fishermen cannot be convinced of this'.[25]

These trespassing cases were heard before Judge J.G. Giffard at Newton county court in December 1885. Twenty people, sixteen men and four women, were each prosecuted for £1 damages for trespass on the oyster beds and Baxter also sought injunctions against future trespass.

Dr Porter goes on to report the test case concerning Ellen Broom, lost at least partly through the ineptness of the solicitor for the defence. James Newton, warned of the dangers of contempt of court, kept up a needle match for several months against Baxter and against Rice, his agent, before he tired of periodic stays in Exeter prison.

Five more young Teignmouth men were to be prosecuted in 1887; but this time they had a champion in the Hon. Bernard Coleridge, M.P. Bernard John Seymour Coleridge was born in 1851 and was the eldest son of John Duke, Baron Coleridge. Educated at Eton and Trinity College, Oxford, he built up a flourishing criminal practice on the western circuit. In contrast to this orthodox education he had a radical's interest in lost causes . . . . In the Teignmouth oyster beds conflict his legal expertise and radical interests could be said to coincide.

The trial took place at Exeter before Sir James Charles Matthews and a grand jury chaired by Sir John Duckworth. Two fishermen, Alfred Dodd aged sixteen and George Mudge aged eighteen years, a seventeen-year-old seaman named George Chapman and two sixteen-year-old servants, Stephen Hooper and Walter Withey, were charged under the Malicious Injuries to Property Act 1861 with malicious damage and stealing 604 oysters from Baxter's beds on 13 June 1886.[26] Basically two matters were at issue: first, whether the defendants were there as charged and second, the matter of Comyns' and Baxter's title.[27]

P.C. Wood, the local water bailiff, saw the defendants in an unlighted boat at 9.30 p.m. just above the Shaldon Bridge and so he informed the Rices. Rice's two sons came on to the river and as soon as the defendants saw them they threw things overboard but some 148 oysters remained in their boat. Hooper told them, 'You can't do anything to us,' and Dodd, defiant, said, 'They had lost some, and they will lose more yet'. There was no doubt as to their identity and they could not have been there by accident or ignorance for all except Hooper had previously been employed by Baxter and so knew the limits. In addition two injunctions had previously been issued against Dodd in January 1885 and April 1886. Edward and William Rice gave evidence of the beds being marked by noticeboards, though only one at present remained. Thus there seemed little doubt of the technical guilt of the defendants if Comyns' right was confirmed, so Coleridge set out to undermine that title.

The prosecution had laid stress on the leases granted to Baxter by Comyns and in support of this produced John Gilpin, a Shaldon pilot aged seventy-six, who gave evidence that his father had rented the oyster beds from Comyns half a century ago. William Buckingham, Comyns' solicitor, proved that Baxter had taken over the beds on the Gilpins surrendering their lease and that the Manors of Bishopsteignton, Radway and West Teignmouth had been legally granted and given away by the Bishop and Dean and Chapter in 1549 under a licence from Edward VI. Comyns himself gave evidence of perambulating the manor bounds and that there were two boundary stones in the middle of the river, that he controlled the river bed and was paid a toll for sand and stone removed from it.[28]

This was a formidable case against Coleridge. To attempt to dent it he first stressed the importance of the beds to employment in Teignmouth, asking Edward Rice, 'Don't you know there are hundreds of families who have earned their livelihood by picking mussels on this shore?' Rice denied it, believing that while some raked mussels in Lord Clifford's manor it was only 'in this last three years' that Baxter's right had been challenged. James William Barnard, Baxter's London manager, said only a few score men and boys were employed.

This line of attack was not very promising so Coleridge asked Comyns if he knew of a statute of James I enabling persons in Devon and Cornwall to take sand from the foreshore and accused him, 'You and other Lords of Manors are converting the estuary of the Teign into a private lake'. Comyns denied all this and reasserted his right. Coleridge then argued that 'by the common law of England the public at large had a right to fish for regular swimming fish, and mussels, and all kinds of oysters between high and low water mark in any navigable river where the sea ebbed and flowed, and they possessed that right independently of the ownership of the soil'. He further claimed that Magna Carta prevented the Crown from granting away the people's fisheries.

To support the public right two old Teignmouth residents were called. Sarah Bowens said she had fished for mussels, cockles and winkles for as long as she could remember over a four mile stretch from the Lower Quay to Flow Point and had never been stopped. William Pook, a fisherman for fifty-five years also proved he had taken mussels, periwinkles and cockles.

However, Coleridge's appeal to common law and custom was unlikely to overcome the contemporary desire to protect the rights of private property, Baxter's investment and the public policy embodied in the Malicious Injuries to Property Act of 1861. In summing up Sir James Matthews made this clear: 'The act under which the prosecution was brought was clear and intelligible. If the beds were clearly marked out then they should be found guilty, though a severe penalty was not called for. There was an abundance of evidence that until recently Baxter was content to treat his oyster bed as an oyster bed and did not object to the people of the locality wandering over the shore and taking mussels, periwinkles and cockles. He did this as an indulgence. But his oyster broods having been damaged he refused to allow the public over the beds'.

The jury agreed, found the prisoners guilty and Matthews ordered each defendant to put up a £10 surety not to touch the oysters again.

Consequently the customary rights which the fishermen felt they had in common law in tidal waters were further diminished. They had indeed little chance in a legal system which increasingly set the rights of private property above those of public custom.

— 5 —
SMALL BOATS ON EAST DEVON BEACHES

Coastline without a Harbour

In the medieval period both the Axe and Otter estuaries were open to the modest-sized ships of the time. Both sent regular if unspectacular contingents to the royal war fleets.

The antiquary Leland, writing during the reign of Henry VIII, described Axmouth as an 'olde and bigge fischar toune'. The same writer described how the Seaton folk had attempted to breach the pebble ridge and the men of Beer to build a quay. In Leland's time, the Otter estuary was 'clene barred'. At some point in the latter half of the sixteenth century Axmouth harbour mouth also became choked.

Evidence exists to show that the two estuaries of East Devon did not remain permanently blocked – lime-kilns were built at both Budleigh and Otterton in the opening years of the nineteenth century, for example.

However the closure of the only two possible harbours in the broad segment of Lyme Bay between Exmouth and the Cobb at Lyme Regis itself for long periods did have an impact on fishing methods. The techniques and traditions of small-boat fishing which had already grown up at such places as Beer and Sidmouth became all important.

Efforts to reopen the shingle-blocked estuaries or to construct quays in the same segment of Lyme Bay were not lacking. In the early 1600s the Earle family made expensive and unsuccessful attempts to reopen Axmouth harbour. Denys Rolle, in 1789, had ideas of forming a harbour at the mouth of the Otter. Acts of Parliament for harbours at Beer (1792 and 1820) and at Sidmouth (1836) were also passed without achieving any result.

The only effort to meet even qualified success was that of J.H. Hallett at Axmouth. This was reported by the brothers Lysons in 1822:

'Piers have been constructed at the mouth of the Axe under the shelter of which vessels of 100 tons discharge their cargoes in safety.'

Ferry house and warehouse on the Axe,

In 1830 Hallett obtained an Act of Parliament to allow quay dues to be collected and the proceeds to be used for the upkeep of the harbour.

G.P.R. Pulman's *Book of the Ax*, published in 1875, speaks of the railway as the reason why the harbour was once more abandoned. Axmouth is once again a centre of attention, although it is now intended to provide shelter for a different type of shipping.

All but the last of these schemes were primarily for commercial shipping.

Because it was designed to give shelter to fishing boats as well as to yachts, details of a little-known scheme of 1863 at Budleigh Salterton are included here. More modest and realistic than most projects, it would have created a tideway into the Otter estuary and enabled smaller craft to shelter behind the pebble ridge. Copies were sent to both the riparian owners, the Hon. Mark Rolle (formerly Trefusis) and Lord Coleridge.

Those familiar with the mouth of the Otter may recall that after 120 years the river again falls into the sea west of the rock ledge and that the struggle between tide and current still forms shifting sand-bars.

The map which accompanies the following letter can be found overleaf.

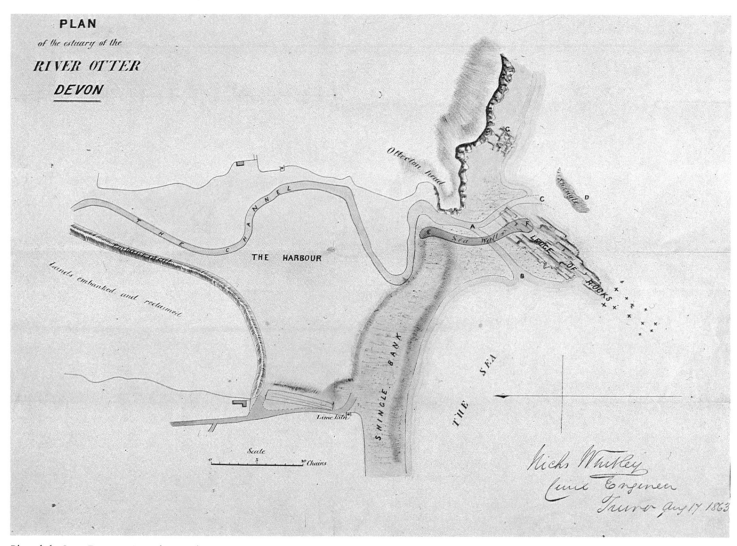

PLAN

of the estuary of the

RIVER OTTER

DEVON

Ottervon Head

THE CHANNEL

THE HARBOUR

Lands embanked and reclaimed

Lime Kiln

SHINGLE BANK

Sea Wall

LEDGE OF ROCKS

THE SEA

Scale

0   5   10 Chains

Nichs Whitley
Civil Engineer
Truro Aug 17. 1863

Plan of the Otter Estuary 1863, showing the sea wall proposed by Nicholas
Whitley with the idea of keeping a channel open for boats (Clinton Devon Estates)

Clovelly, as depicted by the Rev. John Swete in 1797 (Devon Record Office)

Report on the state of the Harbour at the River Otter, Budleigh Salterton, Devon.[1]

Truro August 17th 1863

Sir,

I inspected the estuary of the Otter with Mr Coldridge on the 28th Ulto. and I have since considered the means which it appears most desirable to adopt for the improvement of the entrance of the Harbour, and to keep properly open the outfall of the River, and I now beg to hand you the result of my Survey in this Report with the accompanying sketch plan.

The cause from whence the injury has arisen is no doubt the large increase and accumulation of the Shingle Bank across the entrance of the Harbour, a very narrow Channel only being maintained by the scour of the river at the eastern side of the estuary. The evidence I gathered on the spot went to show that there had been of late years a very large accumulation of Shingle and the width of the Bank is now double that shown on Green's plan made in the year 1808. The general tendency of the shingle is to travel eastward and it has choked up the old mouth of the River from A to B on the plan, and forced the stream to form a new channel for itself from A to C on the eastern side of the ledge. The shingle is now thrown by the surf into this new Channel, and washed to sea by the River freshes, forming a shingle bank at D.

With respect to its Improvement it must first be considered that there is no natural facility for the formation of a convenient Harbour at a moderate cost that the sea going traffic of the neighbourhood is very small and would not justify the expenditure of a sum of money necessary for the construction of a harbour. But that it would be a great benefit to the Inhabitants of the adjoining villages, if small craft, Yachts and fishing Boats could get into the Harbour. And also something requires to be done to protect the mouth of the River from being choked from the constant eastward travelling of the Shingle.

It is evident that no great outlay should be incurred and I am of the opinion that these ends could be obtained by some simple and inexpensive works. I recommend that the Channel be kept in its present course from A to C, having its outfall on the eastern side of the Ledge. That in order to prevent the Travelling of the Shingle into and beyond the Channel, a sea wall be constructed along the eastern crest of the Shingle Bank and across the old channel to the ledge of rocks and marked in Red from E to F on the plan. This wall might be constructed by the materials now on the spot. The large rocks at the foot of the Cliff at G should be placed unhewn to form the base of the wall across the old Channel, and the insterstices [sic] filled, and the remainder of the wall completed with Shingle grouted with blue lias lime having a slope of 4 and 5 to 1 outside and 3 to 1 inside and made 5 feet wide at the Top. This would effectually prevent the Shingle from being washed into the Channel,and as the sea throws up additional Shingle on the slope of the wall it might be grouted and retained so as further to protect the Channel. The ledge of Rocks would prevent any further shingle from being gathered at the mouth of the new Channel at C, and with South West and Westerly winds boats could pull up under the lee of these rocks and reach Harbour in comparatively still water.

Some of the rocks in the new Channel will require to be blown up and removed, and the Channel should be cleared of Shingle and deepened at one or two places.

I consider that these works would keep open the mouth of the River and render the Harbour accessible for small Craft.

The cost of such kind of work it is difficult to estimate – but it would range from £500 to £600.

I am, Sir,
Your most Obedient Servant
Nichs. Whitley

The Small Fishing Boats of East Devon

The next point of reference may be found as well expressed by Reynolds' word-picture of 1908 as anywhere:

Seacombe [Sidmouth] possesses no harbour, and therefore Seacombe men can use no really seaworthy craft. 'Tis all very well', Tony says, 'for people to buzz about the North Sea men an' knit 'em all sorts o' woollen gear. They North Sea men an' the Cornishmen wi' their big, decked harbour boats, they *have* got summut under their feet – somewhere they can get in under, out of the way o' it. They *can* make themselves comfor'able, an' ride out a storm. But if it comes on to blow when we'm to sea in our little open craft, we got to hard up an' get home along – if us can. For the likes o' us, 'tis touch an' go wi' the sea!

Tony knows. At places like Seacombe every boat, returning from sea, must run ashore and be hauled up the beach and even, in rough weather, over the sea wall. The herring and mackerel drifters, which may venture 20 miles into the open sea, cannot be more than 25 feet in length else they would prove unwieldy ashore. To avoid their heeling over and filling in the surf, they must be built shallow, with next to no keel. They have therefore but small hold on the water; they do not sail close to the wind, and beating home against it is a long wearisome job. Again, because the gear for night work in small craft must be as simple as possible, such boats usually carry only a mizzen and a dipping lug – the latter a large, very picturesque, but unhandy, sail which has to be lowered or 'dipped' every time the boat tacks. Neither comfort nor safety is provided by the three feet or so of decking, the 'cuddy' or 'cutty', in the bows. To sleep there with one's head underneath, is to have one's feet outside, and *vice versa*. In rough broken seas the open beach drifter must be handled skilfully indeed, if she is not to fill and sink.[2]

Just because it is verbally expressed, Reynolds' description gives a useful standard to set beside the work of Sidmouth's historian Peter Orlando Hutchinson. Hutchinson was an individualist with an impish sense of humour. (He tells of himself how he asked the policeman guarding the Koh-i-noor diamond at the Great Exhibition of 1851 'were the public allowed to handle the article?') He was also a colourist and draftsman who worked with skill and accuracy and the records he has left are invaluable evidence. Several of his sketches which record different aspects of the lugger-rigged boat will be found in the present work. We have become so used to the 'shark's-fin' silhouette of the racing dinghy that the junk-like outline of the sails of the traditional small boat is something of a surprise.

C.B. Campion and J. Bingley's print of 1831 (below) shows several boats at Sidmouth, two being drawn up on the beach in the foreground. Again reference to Reynolds' work shows us that this record too is substantially accurate. (Notice the short length of decking in the bows.) These boats have a bowsprit, not the short iron bumkin described by Reynolds. It is, however, noticeable that the bowsprit is offset so as not to weaken the stem-post – a clear hallmark of traditional West Country boat and ship construction.

Traditional small boat types have frequently been proved to have evolved at an even earlier period of time than had been suspected. The fully developed type we first see only in 1831 must have had an earlier history.

The two communities at Sidmouth were portrayed with deliberate irony in the print of 1831. The artist and engraver have shown both the boats in the foreground accurately (West Country Studies Library)

At Beer such boats must always have existed. The salt-house there – clearly used in connection with curing fish – was leased by John Lord Rolle in 1813. The lessee was John Ford of Branscombe, founder of the fortunes of the talented and resourceful family who later owned the 'Look Out'.[3]

In 1764 the Beer fishermen were resisting the payment of tithe on fish and were supported, for her own reasons, by 'Madam' Walrond of Bovey House.[4]

A case was heard in the Bishop of Exeter's Consistory Court on 22 October 1613 as to tithes of fish in the parish of Seaton with Beer. A 'share' equal to that of any single one of the partners among the 'Saynemen' was claimed as tithe. William Cawlay 'whole . . . or parte owner of a Sayne and bote . . .' was taking £100 worth of fish in a year and had denied the tithe to Paynter, the vicar. The entry is interesting as showing that in the seventeenth century the small boat was being used at Beer in connection with a very different method of fishing, in recent times more often associated with Cornwall.[5]

In Leland's time (c.1540) an attempt was made to construct a pier – again the involvement of fishermen may be inferred.

Even with such random documentation as this, it is clear that the time at which the typical East Devon fishing boat evolved must remain a question for experts.

The Fishing Community - A Personal View

Campion and Bingley's print of Sidmouth in 1831 may strike us as an interesting, if unremarkable, piece of early nineteenth-century topographical art. A second glance shows that the artist and his engraver are trying to tell us about something more than just the appearance of the place. In the foreground are the fisherfolk: at a distance, riding, promenading and exchanging courtesies, are the 'quality' folk. In brief there were two Sidmouths: the fishing community and the fashionable resort.

Stephen Reynolds (born at Devizes in 1881, died at Sidmouth in 1919) became the exponent of the fishing community with the publication of his books early in the present century. Turning from his middle-class background he lived with a remarkable fisher-family, the Woolleys (Widgers in the books), identified himself with them and was in turn accepted as rather more than a lodger.

The following passages from A Poor Man's House, published in 1908, have been chosen at random to illustrate the skills and methods of the Sidmouth fishermen and something of their home lives as well.

Tony declares that he will really and truly start mackerel hooking tomorrow morning – 'if 'tis vitty', and 'if the drifters an't catched nort,' and 'if tis wuth it,' and 'if he du'.

A creaking and shaking in the timbers of the old house, very early this morning, must have awakened me; then there was a muffled rap on my door. 'Be 'ee goin' to git up?'

'Yes . . . 'Course . . . What time is it?'

The answer was a *pad-pad-pad* down the stairs. I looked out over the bedclothes. The window, a grey patch barred with darker grey, was like a dim chilly ghost gazing at me from the opposite wall. By the saltiness of the damp air which blew across the room and by the grind of the shingle outside, I could tell that the wind was off sea. The sea itself was almost invisible – a swaying mistiness through which the white horses rose and peeped at one, as if to say, 'Come and share our frolic. Come and ride with us'.

Tony, sleepy and sheepish in the eyes, was pattering about the kitchen in his stockings (odd ones), his pants and his light check shirt. The fire was contrary. We scraped out ashes; poked in more wood and paper. Soon a gush of comfortable steam made the lid of the kettle dance. The big blue tin teapot was washed out, filled and set on the hob. The cupboards and front room were searched for cake. Tony went upstairs with a cup o' tay for the ol' doman and came down with a roll of biscuits. (Mrs Widger takes the biscuits to bed with her as maiden ladies take the plate basket, and for much the same reason.)

Faint light was showing through the north window of the kitchen. 'Coom on!' said Tony. 'Time we was to sea.' He refilled the kettle, hunted out an old pair of trousers, rammed himself into a faded guernsey and picked up three mackerel lines[6] from the dresser. He took some salted lasks from the brine-pot, blew out the lamp – and forth we went. After collecting together mast, sails and oars from where they were lying, strewn haphazard on the beach, we pushed and pulled the *Cock Robin* down to the water's edge, and filled up the ballast-bags with our hands, like irritable, hasty children playing at shingle-pies. 'A li'l bit farther down. Look out! Jump in. Get hold the oars', commanded Tony. With a cussword or two (the oars had a horrid disposition to jump the thole-pins) we shoved and rowed off, shipping not more than a couple of buckets of water over the stern. Tony scrambled aboard over the starboard bow, his trousers and boots dripping. ''Tis al'ays like that, putting off and thees yer damn'd ol' baych. No won'er us gits the rheumatics.' He hung the rudder, loosed the mizzen. I stepped the mast, hoisted the jib and lug, and made fast halyards and sheets. Our undignified bobbing, our impatient wallowing on the water stopped short. The wind's life entered into the craft. She bowed graciously to the waves. With a motion compounded of air and water, wings and a heaving, as if she were airily suspended over the sea, the *Cock Robin* settled to her course. Spray skatted gleefully over her bows and the wavelets made a gurgling music along the clinker-built strakes of her.

Tony put out the lines: tangled two of them, got in a tear, as he calls it, snapped the sid, bit the rusty hook off, spat out a shred of old bait, brought the boat's head too far into the wind, cursed the flapping sail and cursed the tiller, grubbed in his pockets for a new hook, and made tiny knots with clumsy great fingers and his teeth. 'An't never got no gear like I used tu', he complained, and then, standing upright, with the tiller between his legs and a line in each outstretched hand, he unbuttoned his face and broke into the merriest smiles. 'What du 'ee think o' Tony then, getting in a tear fust start out? Do 'ee think he's maazed – or obsolete? But we'll catch 'em if they'm yer. Yu ought to go 'long wi' Uncle Jake. He'd tell 'ee summut – and the fish tu if they wasn't biting proper!'

By the time the lines were out, the dun sou'westerly clouds all around had raised themselves like a vast down-hanging fringe, a tremendous curtain, ragged with inconceivable delicacy at the foot, between which, and the water-line, the peep o' day stared blankly. The whitish light, which made the sea look deathly cold, was changed to a silvery sheen where the hidden cliffs stood. From immaterial shadows, looming over the surf-line, the cliffs themselves brightened to an insubstantial fabric, an airy vision, ruddily flushed, till, finally, ever becoming more earthy, they upreared themselves, high-ribbed and red, bush-crowned and splashed with green – our familiar, friendly cliffs, for each and every part of whom we have a name. The sun slid out from a parting of clouds in the west, warming the dour waves into playfulness.

'Twas all a wonder and a wild delight.

As I looked at Tony, while he glanced around with eyes that were at once curiously alert and dreamy, I saw that, in spite of use and habit, in spite of his taking no particular notice of what the sea and sky were like, except so far as they affected the sailing of the boat – the dawn was creeping into him. Many such dawns have crept into him. They are a part of himself.

'Look to your lew'ard line!' he cried, 'they'm up for it!'

He hauled a mackerel aboard, and, catching hold of the shank of the hook, flicked the fish into the bottom of the boat with one and the same motion that flung the sid overboard again; and after it the lead. Wedging the mackerel's head between his knees, he bent its body to a curve, scraped off the scales near its tail, and cut a fresh lask from the living fish. He is a tenderheart by nature, but now: 'That'll hae'em!' he crowed.

The mackerel bit hotly at our new baits. Before the lines were properly out, in they had to come again. Flop-flop went the fish on the bottom-boards as we jerked them carelessly off the hooks. Every moment or two one of them would dance up and flip its tail wildly; beat on the bottom-boards a tattoo which spattered us with scales; then sink back among the glistening mass which was fast losing its beauty of colour, its opalescent pinks and steely blues, even as it died and stiffened.

Suddenly the fish stopped biting, perhaps because the rising sun was shining down into the water. The wind dropped without warning, as southerly winds will do in the early morning, if they don't come on to blow a good deal harder. The *Cock Robin* wallowed again on the water. 'We'm done!' said Tony. 'Let's get in out o' it in time for the early market. There ain't no other boats out. Thees yer ought to fetch 'levenpence the dizzen. We've made thees day gude in case nort else don't turn up.'

While I rowed ashore, he struck sail, and threw the ballast overboard. Most pleasantly does that shingle ballast plop-rattle into the water when there is a catch of fish aboard. We ran in high upon a sea. Willing hands hauled the *Cock Robin* up the beach: we had fish to give away for help. The mackerel made elevenpence a dozen to Jemima Caley, the old squat fishwoman who wears a decayed sailor hat with a sprig of heather in it. 'Yu don' mean to say yu've a catched

all they lovely fish!' she said with a rheumy twinkle, in the hope of getting them for tenpence.

'Levenpence a dozen, Jemima!'

'Aw well then, yu must let I pay 'ee when I sold 'em. An't got it now. Could ha' gived 'ee tenpence down.'

With a mackerel stuck by the gills on the tip of each finger, I came in the house. The children were being got ready for school. When I returned downstairs with some of the fishiness washed off, Mrs Widger was distributing the school bank-cards and Monday morning pennies. (By the time the children leave school, they will have saved thus, penny by penny, enough to provide them with a new rig-out for service – or Sunday wear.) There was a frizzling in the topsy-turvy little kitchen.

'Mam! Vish!'

'Mam! I wants some vish. Mam 'Idger . . .'

'Yu shall hae some fish another time.'

'No-o-o!'

'Go on!'

'Well, jam zide plaate then.'

Jimmy's finger was in the jampot.

'Yu daring rascal!' shrieks Mam Widger. 'Get 'long to school with 'ee! Yu'll be late an' I shall hae the 'spector round. Get 'long – and see what I'll hae for 'ee when yu comes back.'

'Coo'h! Bulls' eyes! Ay, Mam? Good bye, Dad. Good bye, Mam. Bye, Mister Ronals. Gimme a penny will 'ee?'

'God damm the child – that ever I should say it – get 'long! I'll hae a bull's eye for 'ee. Now go on.'

A tramp of feet went on through the passage.

Sundown is the time for shooting nets. Eight to fourteen are carried for mackerel, six to ten for herrings – for the scantier the fish, the greater the number of nets. At Seacombe they are commonly 40 fathoms in length along the headrope which connects them all, and 5 fathoms deep. Stretching far away from the boat, as it drifts up and down the Channel with the tides, is a line, perhaps 1000 yards long, of cork buoys. From these hang the lanyards which support the headrope, from the headrope hang perpendicularly the nets themselves. Judgement is needed in shooting a fleet of nets. They may get foul of the bottom or of another boat's fleet. When, on account of careless shooting or tricks of the tide, the nets of several boats become entangled, there is great confusion, and the cursing is loud.

Nets shot, the fishermen make fast the road for'ard; sup, smoke, sing, creep under the cutty, and sleep with one eye open. Sometimes they are too wet to sleep; often in the winter it is too cold.

Afterwards, the laborious hauling in – one man at the headrope and the other at the foot. Contrary to a very general impression, the fish are not enclosed within the net, as in seining or in pictures of the miraculous draught of fishes. They prod their snouts into the meshes, and are caught by the gills. There may not be a score in a whole fleet of nets, or they may come up like a glittering mat, beyond the strength of two men to lift over the gunwale. Twenty-five thousand herring is about the burthen of an open beach drifter. If there are more, nets must be given away at sea, or buoyed up and left – or cut, broken, lost. Small catches are picked out of the nets as they are hauled in, large catches are landed ashore.

It is ashore that the fishermen comes off worst of all. Neither educated nor commercialized, he is fleeced by the buyers. And if he himself dispatches his haul to London ... Dick Yeo once went up to Billingsgate and saw his own fish sold for about £10. On his return to Seacombe, he received £3 odd, and a letter from the salesman to say that there had been a sudden glut in the market. Fishermen boat-owners have an independence of character which makes it difficult for them to combine together effectively, as wage-servers do. They act too faithfully on the adage that a bird in the hand is worth two in the bush, and 10s. on the beach a sovereign at Billingsgate. So 'tis, when: 'There's little to earn and many to keep', and no floating capital at a man's disposal.

In recent years, owing to bad prices and seasons and general lack of encouragement, or even of fair opportunity, the number of sea-going drifters at Seacombe has decreased by two-thirds. Much the same has happened at other small fishing places along the coast. This decline – so complacently acquiesced in by the powers that be – is of national importance; for the little fisheries are the breeding ground of the navy. Nowadays fishermen put their sons to work on land. 'Tain' wuth it,' they say, 'haulin' yer guts out night an' day, an' gettin' no forrarder at the end o'it.'[7]

The Fishing Community – An Official Record

During the latter half of the nineteenth century considerable attention was paid both to the conditions of fishing boats and to fishery management. Under the provisions of the Sea Fisheries Act of 1868 even small fishing boats were to be registered, and such a register exists for the port of Exeter, 1869–95. Registration was to be in classes. On 1 March 1869 no less than 163 certificates were issued for small boats within the area of administration, as follows:

Budleigh Salterton	Nos. 1 to 30	2nd Class	30
	Nos. 31 to 40	3rd Class	10
Ladram	Nos. 41 to 42	3rd Class	2
Sidmouth	Nos. 43 to 79	2nd Class	37
	Nos. 80 to 92	3rd Class	13
Exmouth	Nos. 93 to 106	2nd Class	14
	Nos. 107 to 139	3rd Class	33
Starcross	Nos. 140 to 144	3rd Class	5
Cockwood	Nos. 145 to 147	3rd Class	3
Powderham	Nos. 148 to 149	3rd Class	2
Topsham	Nos. 150 to 163	2nd Class	14

It can be seen that no first-class certificates were granted. Examination of the record makes it clear that the classes were based on size; third-class boats were propelled by oars only.

Because of the necessity of launching and landing craft from a beach the majority of entries are boats of 1 or 2 tons only, with a 12- or 14-foot keel. Larger boats fall into progressively smaller groups at between 3 tons (18-foot keel) and a single 12-ton boat (31-foot keel) which was based at Starcross. Boats of 5–10 tons were not exclusive to Exmouth or the Exe estuary. The Minnow of Budleigh Salterton was of 9 tons with a 26-foot keel. Such a vessel must have been beached (and launched) by windlass. (The register in fact does include eleven vessels from Lyme Regis including a decked trawler of 17 tons.)

After 1886 instructions were given for boats to be put in a single series allocated numbers in a single sequence and for each to retain a single number while remaining on the register. The highest registration number was 362, but with allocation of new numbers and re-registration, the volume includes some 756 entries distributed as follows:

Beer	79
Branscombe	11
Sidmouth	180
Ladram	4
Budleigh Salterton	107
Exmouth	186
Exe estuary	208

Unlike the totals given for the initial registration, these numbers do not of course give the total of boats in use at any one time, but they do give a scale of comparative importance.

In the absence of motor power, propulsion was, of course by oars or sail, often by both. Boats with some form of lugsail rig far outnumber those propelled by oars alone or those with a cutter rig. (The characteristic appearance of this rig is well illustrated in the 'fun' watercolour of the stranded whale by Peter Orlando Hutchinson reproduced at the beginning of the book.)

Among fishing methods, seine, drift and trawl nets are all recorded, and, by no means exclusively in the Exe estuary, lobsters, crabs and shellfish were caught. Many boat-owners clearly wished to keep their options open and asked that one or more operations or even 'general fishing' be entered in the register. The predominant methods were however 'hooking' or 'hook and line', the latter, particularly when undertaken by one man, requiring strength, skill and concentration, as described in the following passage from A Poor Man's House:

Anyhow, I wound up the mackerel line; my catch, nill. Such an occurrence makes one very respectful towards the fisherman who singlehanded can sail his boat and manage five mackerel lines at once – one on the thwart to lew'ard and one to wind'ard; a bobber on the mizzen halyard and two bobbers on poles projecting from the boat. He must keep his hands on five lines, the tiller and the sheet; his eyes on the boat's course, the sea, the weather and the luff of the sail.

SEA FISHERIES' ACT, 1868, 31 and 32 Vict., cap. 45.

TABLE A.

Port of _Exeter_

Date of Registry. 1870	Name of Vessel.	Port or Place to which belonging.	Name of Owner.	Name of Master.	Of Vessel or Boat, how Rigged, what Sails used, &c.	Ordinary mode of Fishing.	1st. Class.	2nd. Class.	3rd. Class.	Tonnage.	Length of Keel.	Men.	Boys.
Novr 21	Little Sarah	Topsham	Albert Hall	Albert Hall	Lug Sails	Lining		323			1	16	4	
Decr 1	Ringleader	Exmouth	Thomas Pincombe	Thomas Pincombe	Open Boat, Lug Sail	Net & line		324		3	22	4	
" 17	Gipsy	do	Edward Bradford	Edward Bradford	do.	do		325		2	21	3	
1871. Jan 5	Lucky Alfred	Sidmouth	John Hook Jr	John Hook Jr	do	Hooking drifting		326		1½	14	2	
" 17	Eliza	Exmouth	William Perriam	William Perriam	Rowing Boat, Lug Sail	Hook & line		327		1	14	1	
	Eliza _Former Registry Er 300 & 286._	do	Thomas Balmano	Thomas Balmano	Open Boat, Lug Sail	do		328		1	14		
Feb 3	Ann & Mary	do.	Samuel Turner	Samuel Turner	Rowing Boat	Hook			329	½	10½	1	
" 15	Sea Dream	Budleigh Salterton	William Rogers	William Rogers	Open Boat, Lug & mizzen	Hooking &c		330		1½	12½	2	
" 21	Sea Gull _Former Registry Er 279_	Exmouth	Joseph Copp	Joseph Copp	do	Nets & lines		331		3	24	4	
" 25	Mary	Ladram	Henry Bolt	Henry Bolt	Rowing Boat	Hooking &c			332	1	11½	1	
March 1	Eliza	Starcross	John Pool	John Pool	Open Boat, Lug Sail	Line		333		1	13	1	
" 14	Shannon	Exmouth	George Carpenter	George Carpenter	do.	do		334		1	13	1	
" 24	Teaser	Topsham	George Murphy	Richard Murphy	do.	Luning		157		1	18	4	
" "	Mind me well	do.	do.	do.	do.	do.		152		1	22	9	
" "	Up	do.	do.	do.	do.	do.		155		1	15	4	
" "	Fox	do.	do.	do.	do.	do.		156		1	19	4	
" "	Good Intent	do.	do.	do.	do.	Drifting		159		1	23	4	
" 30	do.	Sidmouth	Wm & Edwd Bartlett	Edward Bartlett	Rowing Boat	Leining			80	3½	22	6	

Registration of fishing craft, 1868

Above:
*Appledore from the fishing weir on the foreshore at Instow, c.1795. William
Payne (West Country Studies Library)*

Right
*Sloops (or Smacks) off Combe Martin, from a hand-coloured lithograph of 1814.
These typical small merchant vessels, says Michael Nix, were used for fishing
during the winter months to earn their keep (West Country Studies Library)*

A more personal touch is provided by the appearance in the record of well known fishing families. Samuel Woolley of Sidmouth registered the *Britannia* between 1874 and 1894 and George Woolley, also of Sidmouth, the *Sea Foam* between 1888 and 1894. These men were members of the remarkable family who provided information to J. Tindall for his observations on the constant changes in Sidmouth's foreshore (*Sidmouth Shingle*), and with whom Stephen Reynolds lodged in the years after 1906.

Exmothians will need no introduction to Edward Bradford, who registered the *Gipsy* in December 1870, or to Thomas James Rowsell (master) and Albert Arthur Rowsell (owner) of the *Olive Branch*, registered in May 1886.

At Lympstone John D. Challis was the master and owner of no less than three boats first registered in March 1869 – the *Ellen, Mary Ann* and *Wave*: multiple registrations are comparatively rare.[8]

This and information like it may be culled from what is apparently so dead and boring a source. No register is available for what could be an even more fascinating period – that of the transition from oar and sail to motor power.

Mrs Bartlett was alarmed by the damage done to her husband's nets by a cow on 19 February 1876. Mr P.O. Hutchinson had only tried to be helpful by allowing them to be dried on his fence. The sketch includes a representation of himself, on the left, wearing a hat (West Country Studies Library)

NETS, WEIRS AND 'PRIVILEGED ENGINES'
IN THE RIVERS OF NORTH DEVON

The North Devon Coast

Clovelly, the pattern of the cliff-hung fishing village, Appledore and Lynton, picturesque if not so timeless, were all once bustling, smelly places of business. Their wealth in the sixteenth and into the seventeenth century was founded on the shoals of pilchards and herring which then swarmed each year up the Bristol Channel.

At Clovelly the quay was built by George Cary, an eminent lawyer (*d.* 1601). He thereby returned a part of the fortune made during his highly remunerative career to the place where he was first and foremost the squire. As late as 1822 there were still sixty or seventy boats employed for two months of the year, and even so the fishery was described as 'much failed'. The Reverend John Robbins, vicar from 1730 to 1777, recorded Clovelly's fortunes in the parish register between 1740 and 1746. His record conveys a quite unintentional sense of comic anticlimax.

> 'In this Year 1740 God was pleased to send his blessing of a great Fishery amongst us after a failure of many years. This thro' his mercy continued in 1741. In this year 1742 the fish was small & poor & in less quantities. In this year 1743 but an indifferent fishing. In this year 1744 worse than in the preceeding. In the year 1745 still worse. In the year 1746 much worse.'[1]

At which point, thankfully, the catalogue of disaster ceases!

Early in 1602, we learn from records of the Bishop of Exeter's Consistory Court that one Popham to whom the tithes of Northam, Lynton and Countisbury had all been leased instituted proceedings in respect of unpaid tithes of fish. From these we learn that if fishermen set out from and returned to the same port, where they then landed their fish, they were then expected to pay tithe in respect of those fish.

At Northam John Davie, William Bennet, Richard Jewell, Richard Whitstone, Richard Bishop and William Jefferies, fishermen (all surely from Appledore), were all accused of evading tithe payments of their catches of herring in the river of 'Severon' or main sea.[2]

Steamer and fishing vessels off Lynmouth about the year 1840 (West Country Studies Library)

In the case of Lynmouth we read that between September and December 1601, John Wood neglected to pay tithe on the 500 'meaze' of herring he landed during that period. We learn in the Oxford English Dictionary that the 'mease' (a suitable word for use in *Call My Bluff*, perhaps) was a measure of herring reckoned at 500 fish at least, but in North Devon at least 612 of them. A 'mease' was reckoned to be worth 5s. at that date and Wood had, it was alleged, kept back tithes to the value of £12.10s. This gives an idea of the riches of the Bristol Channel fishery at that time.[3]

Sadly, however, Lynmouth was the victim of a freak storm in 1607,[4] as well as in 1952. The floodwater washed away the fish curing houses which were then built on the beach. Without outside aid or subsidy to rebuild the shattered community they were never fully reinstated and Lynmouth's fishery suffered a premature decline. No longer could the fishermen 'goynge fourthe out of the said haven or Creeke of Lynemouth . . . in any boate or vessell into the Ryver of Seaverne or mayne Sea adioynynge a Fishynge . . . there take fishe, viz. Congers, Lynges, Milwilles, Gurnardes, thornebackes, whitinges, hearringes, pilchardes or any of them or the like with their nettes hookes and other Engynnes' in such abundance.*

If there was such an abundance of fish in the Bristol Channel in the sixteenth and seventeenth centuries, hardly less astounding were the riches of the rivers Taw and Torridge and their estuary in the eighteenth century. No less than 17 239lbs of salmon was taken in one year from the fisheries of Denys Rolle of Hudscott. He owned two weirs, Beam on the Torridge and Umberleigh on the Taw, fitted with hatches or box traps. In these the salmon were most unsportingly caught and easily drawn forth.

Because the river fishery of North Devon is so much more fully documented, it is this that will be examined in this section.

For example, we learn of a grant in 1260 from the Bishop of Exeter to Henry Tracy to make a salmon pool by his mill at Bishop's Tawton and of an agreement in the same year between Joan de Champernowne and William Fitzwaryn as to Umberleigh Weir. Just how full a story can be compiled on one feature of a river will be seen from the Prebendary Andrews' article which follows.

Umberleigh Weir

Umberleigh Weir, 8 miles south of Barnstaple, is the last weir on the River Taw. From bank to bank it is no less than 316 yards in length, the weir proper at the northern end next the mill being continued southwards by a wall which incorporates two islands. The boundary dividing the parish of Atherington on the left bank from that of Chittlehampton on the right has the unusual effect of leaving the weir proper and the northern island in the former, the long southern island and two sluices being in the latter. More to the point, the mill, the mill ditch, and the weir proper were part of the manor of Umberleigh, but half the long wall with its two sluices which could render the mill useless belonged to the manor of Brightley. From time to time the lords of these manors were not content with peaceful co-existence. It may not be without significance that there appears to be no recorded marriage between the families which successively owned them, despite the general truth of Dr Johnson's observation that 'Proximity makes marriages'.

*The weirs on Lynton beach will feature later in this article.

Salmon caught in the River Taw, 1756. Judging from the price given for almost 1100lbs salmon, the total catch for the year must have been some 15 900lbs! (Clinton Devon Estates)

The first document (1260) contains the seeds of possible discord: 'In the 44th year of the reign of King Henry Son of King John It was agreed in this manner between Joan de Champernowne the Lady of Womberleigh of the one part and William Fitzwaryn Lord of Brithleigh of the other part that is to say That the aforesaid John for herself and her heirs hath granted given and confirmed to the aforesaid William 2s. of yearly rent and liberty to grind at the Mill of Womberleigh freely without toll whensoever and at all times for ease for the hatched weir of Womberleigh and other easements whatsoever there to be granted at the weir aforesaid And it is likewise agreed between Joan Lady of Womberleigh and Wm Fitzwaryn Lord of Brithleigh that all Fish taken there in Weels hatches nets or any other Engines be faithfully divided between them as can best be devised by lot at every time of the year And if it happen that I the aforesaid Joan or my heirs the said hatches in the weir aforesaid for taking the fish at any time do not as agreed upon keep up repair or maintain for our common advantage by default whereof any loss shall arise. Then it shall be lawful to the aforesaid William and his heirs the hatches of the weir aforesaid to obstruct and the easement whatsoever to bar and impede for ever In testimony whereof the parties aforesaid to this writing of agreement to endure for ever have put their seals – These being witnesses Sir Hugh le Touch Sir Henry Tracey Sir Roger Beaupel Knights Lawrence Conrad John Wyncote Philip de Scatforde Chaplain of the said Joan and many others.'[5]

The next document is of the year 1527, by which time Umberleigh had passed to the family of Basset, and Brightley to that of Coblegh, whose heiress had married Roger Giffard, a younger son of Giffard of Halsbury. It is a complaint by Honor Basset, widow of John Basset, Knight, to the Court of Star Chamber. 'One Roger Gyfford gentleman, David Hancock yeoman, David Richard yeoman, and divers other evilly disposed persons to the number of VIII persons . . . with forse of armys, at XII at Clocke yn the nyghte of the 17th day of September, put down the Skluys called the Fender of the water of the sayd myll dyche and the same fender neyled fast As well under the water as above intending thereby the destruccon of the sd myll . . . And then and ther the seid Roger Gifford etc forssibly fysshed and took as well a grett number of Salmons as other fysshe And further the sd David Richard with Thomas Mannyn and others the nygthe of the 20th day of the same month by the commaunment of oon John Coblegh Esq ryottosly ffysshed the sd myll dych and took 11 or 12 Salmon and assaulted two of the servants of the sd Sir John Basset named Raff Bamfylde and Simon Rede . . . whereupon Sir John Bassett exhibited a bill of complnt and his servant was to have delivered several writs of subpoena against John Coblegh Roger Gifford etc . . . at the parish church of Chittelhampton but while he was at the high altar at Mass the Sunday before Christmas the said David Hancock and one Hugh Welshman servant of John Coblegh furiously with drawn swords and bucklers holding in their hands attacked the said John Bery and would have murdered him if he had not defended himself and again the same day with John Mudde and others lay in wait in the highway between the church of Chittlehampton and the house of John Bassett with the intent to murder the said John Bery . . .'[6]

The depositions appended to this petition are dated 7 May 1529. John Coblegh is said to be forty-nine, Roger Giffard thirty-seven.

Honor Basset married secondly Arthur Plantagenet, Viscount Lisle, who took up his wife's case.

Quoting at length from a Star Chamber Petition, Prebendary Andrews shows how Viscount Lisle petitioned William Courtenay Knight and Baldwyn Mallet Esq., the King's justices at Exeter Assizes, to make an award to settle the disputes between his wife and Cobleigh and Gyfford. At great expense the mills themselves, 26 miles from Exeter, were viewed and the parties sworn to abide by the arbitration. Viscount Lisle might have spared himself the expense, as the account goes on to relate a story of double-dealing. As always the petition is couched in terms of formal outrage (the reply, doubtless in tones of injured innocence, has not survived).

'. . . and furdermore then and ther at the same tyme before the said Justices ther was ferder faithfull promyse and aggrement hadde and takyn between your said beseecher and the said John Coblegh and Roger Gifford that they . . . schold cum to London before the fest of All Seyntes then next comyng and ther to geve ther dylygent attendaunce uppon the said arbitratoures for the finall ordinnaunce . . . and your said beseecher therupon tristyng the sayd John Coblegh and Roger Gyfford wold have faithfully fulfyllyd and performyd ther appoyntment . . . at hys grett costes expenses and charges came from hys dwellyng howse callyd Suberton in your countie of Sowth Hampton to your Cytye off London . . . and ther continued tarying and lokyng for the said John Coblegh and Roger Gyfford by the space of viii or nyne days where they came nott. So hyt ys most dreded Soveraygn lord that the seid John Coblegh and Richard [sic] Gyfford oon Richard Bowden John Harrys John Peperr Hugh Clement Richard Fyvyn John Carse Geffrey Schestrigge John Pelaven Thomas Selerr Thomas Mude John Shepperdre Wyllyam Downe John Skynner John Hogge and Symon Matecotte with dyvers other evyll dysposed persons to the number of xx[ti] persons or ther abowtes to your beseecher unknown yn maner of war arrayed in harnes and with swordes bokelers, arrowes, bylles, holberdes, forest bylles, daggers, stavys, mattocks, shovylls, barrys of iren and peck axys and other wepons bothe invasyve and defensyve as persons are dreding God your hyghnes nor your lawes ne regardyng the seyd appoyntment before your seyd Justices hadde and made . . . but they the second day of November 1530 . . . reygn ryotously with force of armes . . . came to the seyd were and then and ther ryotously and with force ayenst your lawes have not only newly turned and devorted parte off the seyd water of Tawe owte of hys ryght course yn the sowth parte of the seid were to the inusaunce of the seyd myll and severall fyshynges but also utterly dystroyed the seid were and severall fyshynges to the hurt and damages of your beseecher and hys seyd wyff of £200 and also to the grete inuisaunce hurt and damages of your subjectes that all tymes have used frely to fysshe yn the seyd water.' Lord Lisle asks therefore for letters of Privy Seal

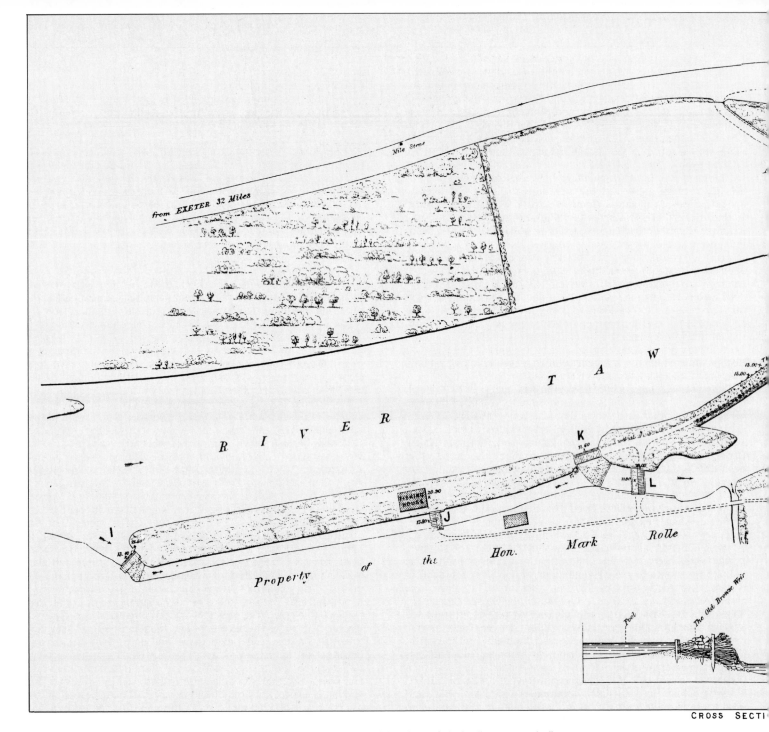

Umberleigh Weir on the River Taw, 1866, showing fish traps 'J' and 'L'; fish pass 'H' and then feed through to Umberleigh Mill (Devon Record Office)

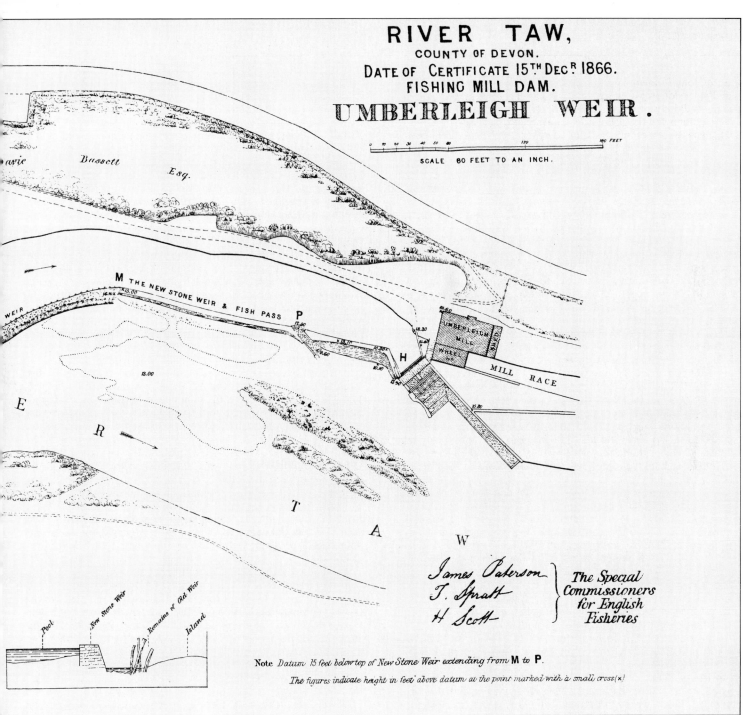

RIVER TAW,
COUNTY OF DEVON.
DATE OF CERTIFICATE 15TH DECR 1866.
FISHING MILL DAM.
UMBERLEIGH WEIR.

SCALE 60 FEET TO AN INCH.

Bassett Esq.

M THE NEW STONE WEIR & FISH PASS P

WEIR

UMBERLEIGH MILL

WHEEL

MILL RACE

H

E
R
T
A
W

13.00

James Paterson
J. Spratt
H. Scott

} The Special Commissioners for English Fisheries

Pool   New Stone Weir   Remains of Old Weir   Island

Note *Datum 15 feet below top of New Stone Weir extending from* **M** *to* **P.**

The figures indicate height in feet above datum at the point marked with a small cross (×)

TO AN INCH.

directing John Coblegh and Roger Giffard etc. to appear before Star Chamber the following Hilary Term.[7] Whatever the settlement of this dispute, it did not produce a lasting peace.

In 1691 John Giffard of Brightley appears in Chancery as plaintiff and Francis Bassett of Umberleigh as defendant. Giffard's case is that by the deed of 44 Henry III, the owners of Umberleigh are to pay 2s. yearly for ever for the tying of the weir, to grind the Brightley corn toll free, and to deliver to the owners of Brightley half the fish taken in the hatches and mill ditch. A dispute having arisen about twenty years previously, the matter had been referred to Sir Thomas Carew, a friend to both parties, who ruled that Giffard was entitled to a moiety of the fish, and the moiety was paid during the lifetime of John Bassett, the then owner. The defendant, Francis Bassett, replies that he believes that some agreement was entered into by his grandfather, who 'much complayned of the said Agreement and often declared that there was noe fish due to the Owners of Brightly and to the end his heires might not pay the same after his death he left a writeing whereby he declared that the two shillings rent and the grinding Toll free were by virtue of an antient custome and that the Deed which the heires of Brightly have was an old rotten scrowle that was never in issue', and further, that the award of Sir Thomas Carew was binding only upon the owner, but not upon the inheritance. The Court orders the parties to proceed to a trial at law before a special jury at the next assizes at Exeter. The depositions of seven witnesses for the plaintiff and four for the defendant are preserved. The cause having been tried at Exeter, with verdict for the plaintiff, order was then given in Chancery, on 29 June 1692, that Giffard and his heirs be established in the quiet and peaceful possession of one moiety of the said fishery for the future, but the plaintiff was not to have any account of one moiety for the time past, and this was to be without costs on either side.[8]

In 1738 Samuel Rolle, of Hudscot in Chittlehampton, who the previous year had bought Brightley from the Giffards, leased the Umberleigh fishery from John Bassett for 21 years.[9] The Bassett family had now moved to Heanton Court, the other noble seat (to use Prince's description) which they had inherited from an heiress of Beaumont. As Prince puts it: 'Here [i.e. at Umberleigh] this family had its first residence after it became theirs; but it being the more melancholy, and less healthful place, they removed hence to Heanton Court. A sweet and pleasant seat it is; a very handsome pile, well furnished with all variety of entertainment, which the earth, and sea, and air, can afford'.[10]

But all was not yet peaceful at the weir. In 1754 Denys Rolle of Hudscot brought a suit against John Paddon, lessee of Umberleigh Mill, alleging the removal of soil at the weir causing the destruction of an acre of land, and claiming £60 damages. The matter was referred to the arbitrament of John Pine of Eastdowne and Thomas Harding of Upcott, whose judgement given in 1756 was that Paddon should pay £17 damages to Rolle, that all suits between should cease, and that the fender belonging to Rolle must be always no lower than the top of the weir belonging to Umberleigh Mill.[11]

Paddon was however soon helping himself to fish of which he rendered no moiety. In 1758 John Smallredge and Charles Row testified that they saw Paddon take one salmon on 14 November, two on the 19th, 'at another time 15 Salmon and he hath been seen to Gaff a Great many more at other times'. The salmon was being sold in High Bickington at 1¼d. a pound. In the following year Rolle began a suit against John Paddon and John Paddon the younger, claiming £200 damages from each for breaking into the Brightley fishery, and a similar amount for breaking into the Umberleigh fishery rented from Bassett, taking from each 'One Thousand Salmons One Thousand Trouts One Thousand Jacks One Thousand Pykes One Thousand Carp One Thousand Tench One Thousand Perch One Thousand Roaches One Thousand Daces One Thousand Eeles and One Thousand Gudgeons'. Paddon denied the charges, and the case came before the assizes. In the summary of evidence to be given for Rolle it was alleged that there used to be a hatch on the weir with two keys, which was only unlocked when the servants of both owners were present, but that this had been destroyed several years, and that Paddon had made it his constant practice to take fish, boasting that it was worth £10 a year to him. Rolle's expenses at the Summer Assizes in 1760 are given as £17. 10s. 4d., but the judgement of the court is not recorded in the papers which have been preserved.[12]

It seems that peace now obtained at the weir. Together with fish taken with boats and nets the fishery in one year made a profit of £69. 17s. 11½d., the price of salmon varying from 3d. to 1¼d. a pound, 16 150 pounds being sold, in addition to 1089 pounds for use at home or given away. In 1781 Denys Rolle received the following offer:

'Atherington Febry the 27 1781 Sqr Rowle we have Taken the Liberty of wraiting thes fue Lains hoping your oner will Take nothing ermis We are In formed that you have not set out your fishing at Umberley Bridg we Should be glad if your oner ould Tak es tenets for the sam We are In formed that you have goat Sqr Bassets Rait of fishing If your oner have we shall be glad to Take boath parts of your oner and com in boath upon convenant If we could but Speke with your oner a bout the Terms of Taken the sam. John alford Calvin Radmoor

We shall be glad if your oner will send us a anser.'[13]

In 1796 Denys Rolle was busy preparing for legal action against Sir Bourchier Wrey, of Tawstock, for alleged obstruction of fish,[14] but this is another long story which has nothing to do with Umberleigh Weir. Proceedings were interrupted by Denys Rolle's death in 1797, but continued by his son, Lord Rolle. Denys Rolle, the richest landowner in Devonshire, died aged 72 while on his usual walk between his seats of Stevenstone and Hudscot (ten miles apart) beneath a tree at Nethercleave, beside the river which had given him so much trouble.[15]

Trouble began again in 1805, when Jos. D. Bassett, writing from Watermouth Castle, where his family had now settled, addressed a respectful but somewhat peremptory letter to Lord Rolle, complaining that the tenant of Brightley had drawn off so much water as to leave too little for the mill. In a further letter of 1806 he observed: '. . . at the time the award was made [i.e. 1756] there was only one fender in the bank of your gut which fender still remains as it then was, but within the last seven years as many fenders more have been added, each lower than the other'. For the other side it was alleged that the miller was losing water because he had failed to keep his own weir in repair. A suit was begun against the tenant of Brightley in 1807, but of its outcome we have no record.[16]

Fish continued for many years to be divided between the two owners. The fish house on the bank of the gut was removed soon after the First World War, and the hatch in which the fish had been taken removed from the west bank of the northern island at the same time. It had not for some years then been used for taking fish.[17] A few years later Umberleigh Mill ceased to grind, and was converted into a charming residence – charming except in high flood.

We may add a postscript to Prebendary Andrews' article from records which were not available to him.

In December 1866 the Special Commissioners for English Fisheries conducted an extremely thorough enquiry into the legality of the Umberleigh Weir. The proceedings included an on-site inspection from which the owners and indeed all other parties were excluded. Interestingly, many of the documents used by Prebendary Andrews for his history were also examined 'in Chambers' by the Commissioners. Certificates of legality were finally issued to Arthur Davie Bassett

and to the Hon. Mark Rolle, the two riperian owners. Even in 1866 the 'hutches' were licensed for a moderate annual fee: there was no fish pass.

By July 1913, the Conservators of the Taw and Torridge Fishery District, presumably reflecting at least a section of public opinion,[18] regarded the licence fee of £9.12s. per annum as totally inadequate compensation for the fish taken and for the denial of the upper reaches of the Taw to fish for breeding. They made the first of several bids to acquire the fishing rights in order to neutralize the barrier formed by the weir. Finally, in 1917 they succeeded in leasing the weir from Mrs Curzon at £15 per annum, the understanding being that fish would be allowed to pass the weir at will.

Conservation on a Shoestring

The Salmon Fishery Amendment Act of 1865 set up a pattern of Boards of Conservators for 'Fishery Districts' based on the river systems of England and Wales. Thus was founded one of the complex group of administrative authorities finally united into the regional Water Authorities in April 1974.

On 11 July 1913 the Clerk to the Board of Conservators of the Taw and Torridge applied to the Public Works Development Board for a loan, which was never received. However his application sets out the Board's aims and terms of reference admirably, not least in specifying the barriers physical and financial, which prevented the realization of its aims.

The weir at Black Torrington, belonging to Rev. W.H. Coham (*Agriculture of the County of Devon*, C. Vancouver, 1808)

My Board constituted under the Salmon Fishery Act 1865 on the 26th day of March 1866 controls the rivers Taw and Torridge and their tributaries and the estuaries of the said rivers and so much of the coast as lies between the western boundary of the County of Somerset and the eastern boundary of the County of Cornwall and all rivers flowing into the sea between the said points and being in the County of Devon. It will be seen therefore that their district is a very large one and there are no funds available other than the licence duties, the dividend on a sum of £100 India stock and the fines received on prosecutions to meet the cost of 4 Water bailiffs, 1 Superintending Water Bailiff, temporary bailiffs from time to time, the costs of the prosecutions and the necessary expenditure in protecting and improving the fishing generally.

With the aid of local subscriptions the board have spent a considerable amount of money in recent years in improving weirs giving easier access to spawning ground and, thereby improving the fishing in the estuary, but much remains to be done and local assistance can no longer be relied upon. The staff of water bailiffs is totally inadequate at certain seasons of the year when the salmon are running up the rivers and returning, for the watching in the estuary is then quite as necessary as at other times and there are also further works requiring attention all of which would ensue to the interest of fishing generally. A fish pass is required at Eggesford weir on the river Taw which would open up a large area of spawning ground and the makeshift pass at Darkham weir on the river Torridge requires improving.

It would also be very desirable to purchase if it could be acquired the fishing right in the boxes or hatches at Umberleigh on the River Taw in which large numbers of salmon which would otherwise ascend that river are taken annually and which are used under sanction of the law and by payment of a licence duty of £9.12s.0d., in a manner prejudicial to the public interest.

My Board would, if it had the funds, pursue scientific research in connection with the marking of salmon and smolts and in tracing the origin and cause of disease in fish such as is now present in the rivers under their care.

If therefore your Board can make my Board a grant the money so granted will be spent in furtherance of the above objects which if accomplished would benefit the fishermen generally and especially those net fishermen in the estuary whose livelihood to a great extent depends upon the abundance of salmon in our rivers.'

Fishing in the Taw – Torridge estuary, with its complex tides and formidable bar, was bound to involve special application of fishing methods. It is of interest to see what these were and how the Board of Conservators attempted both to control their use and to reconcile the sometimes antagonistic claims of different groups of fishermen in the first two decades of the present century. As will be seen they were concerned to preserve fish stocks for the professional net fisherman rather than for the gentleman angler.

'Priviledged Engines'

Fish traps of various kinds are a type of fishing technique particularly suited to estuaries. We know that in 1601 James Hygate, vicar of Fremington, went to law to claim tithes of fish from one Joan Time. The claim included eels caught in weirs. The V-shaped fish weir, which trapped fish on a receding tide, was a structure of some substance and positively medieval crudity – and efficiency.

William Williams of Heanton Court owned two in the Taw estuary, one at Ashford, and another a little to the north, Horsey Weir. The latter lay against the embankment at Horsey Island constructed by Williams in the mid 1850s. An earlier fish weir in the then reclaimed land was not, as Barnstaple shipowners hoped, surrendered, but replaced. Both Ashford and Horsey Weirs were licensed as 'Privileged Engines' in December 1866 by the newly constituted Special Commissioners for English Fisheries.

By January 1912, some forty-five years later, the weir at Ashford had become a risk to shipping and was reported as such to the Board of Trade, as the following extract from minutes of the Board of Conservators for the Taw and Torridge shows. (In the sequel it is clear that the report was duly filed and forgotten!)

Ashford Weir
Supt Gregory reported that on December last he was proceeding down the River Taw from Barnstaple at low water in his boat. On arriving at Ashford Weir, when he considered he was through the weir he came in contact with some of the stakes, but within a few seconds the boat surging around cleared them. 'I had the new boat at the time; if I had had one of the old boats it would very likely have had a hole through the bottom. There was a large fresh going down at the time.'
It *was resolved* on the motion of Mr Pearce and seconded by Mr James Landers
That a copy of the report be sent to the Board of Trade.

For many years, two 'V' weirs were a feature of the Lynmouth foreshore. By 1906 the western weir had been altered so as to form a sheltered semi-tidal swimming pool, but the eastern weir retained its original purpose.

The following report shows how drastically the Fishing Weir had been rebuilt between 1906 and December 1913. the 'certificate' was presumably one issued in 1866 under the Salmon Fisheries Amendment Act.

Lynmouth Weir
Supt Gregory reported on the eleventh instant as follows: 'Acting on instructions received I have inspected the weir at Lynmouth and taken careful measurements on Tuesday, 2 December. I find that it is very different in shape and size to the tracing supplied to me from the original certificate. The weir is of a 'V'-shape with the point of the 'V' facing towards the sea and in the original certificate the two arms are of equal length of about 160 feet each whereas now the arms are

about 195 feet each ... The pieces added at the ends of the arms are of fairly recent work and make the weir a deadly trap for salmon as the west extension runs into the river. The weir seems to have had each of its arms extended towards the south for a distance of some 30 feet and in addition there are the other extensions at the ends of the arms ...'

It was resolved that the Clerk write the owners with a copy of the plan on the original certificate and that if the weir was used in any other form than there shown the Board would have to take action in the matter.

Draft Nets

Tarka the Otter, of course, escaped from one. Hardly less remarkable is the fact that they were used so far up the Torridge as south (i.e. upstream) of Landcross railway bridge.

In this letter of 1914, the Fishery Conservator's legal adviser was concerned with the poor drafting of by-laws and resulting misunderstanding among fishermen that draft netting was banned even in the lower estuary. He was even more concerned with the more than ordinary misuse of draft nets in such a way that they constituted a temporary barrier across the breadth of the rivers. We also learn how they should have been used.

The mention of the 'railway bridge' at Barnstaple is of course ambiguous; perhaps that carrying the spur line between the North Devon and former Devon and Somerset at Seven Brethren Bank was the one referred to.

The Clerk read the following letter received by the Chairman from Mr C.E. Fryer, 31 August 1914: 'I have been very carefully considering the points raised with reference to the by-law recently made ... for regulating fishing above the railway bridges across the River Taw and Torridge respectively near Barnstaple and Landcross.

Very considerable misapprehension appears to exist in the district as to the purport and effect of this by-law. In the first place, it is imagined, and it has been represented, that the by-law would prohibit fishing in the estuary near Appledore. By-law requires that all draft nets for salmon in any part of the district above Braunton shall be used by holding one end of the net on the shore or bank and by shooting the net from a boat which shall start from such shore or bank and return without delay from the shore or bank from which it started and then drawing the net on to such shore or bank.

I understand that, in some recent proceedings under this by-law, it was shown to be the habit of a certain fishman or fishermen to use a draft net in a part of the river above Barnstaple not in the manner described, but by stretching it right across the river and drawing it down from both banks for a distance of from half to three-quarters of a mile. It is not, to my mind, possible to conceive that such a method of fishing is in accordance with the by-law and I would venture to point out that, if this practice is continued, it is for your Board to consider whether they should not make a much more stringent

regulation which might have the effect of entirely prohibiting netting in the part of the river in question.

I, of course, need not point out to you that the object of any regulations under the Fishery Acts is to improve the stock of fish in the river. Neither is it necessary to point out that the recent Royal Commission on salmon fisheries, following previous authorities, made a strong recommendation to the effect that it was desirable and in some cases necessary in the interest of the fisheries to restrict or even entirely to prohibit fishing for salmon in narrow waters such as those above the bridges referred to. It seems to me, therefore, that if the moderate restriction now imposed on the use of draft nets is not observed at the place in question it may be necessary for your Board to consider whether they should not put forward for confirmation a much more stringent regulation.'

Coarse Fishing in Winter

In April 1912 Water Bailiff Pidler, stationed at Instow, reported on inspection of the boats of fishermen in the estuary. The object was to monitor the effects of a new by-law permitting the use of a net with a 1½ inch mesh between 16 December until the last day of February (until February of 1915).

Coarse Fishing under the New By-Laws

Supt Gregory reported that he had obtained the following information relating to fishing for coarse fish under the new by-laws:

Extracted from Water Bailiff Pidler's log book:

1911 Decr 19   1 boat in the estuary had about 5 draughts and caught about 20lbs of cod, bass & flukes

Decr 21   1 boat at Capstone bay two draughts and 1 at the Weeds, caught about 20lbs of bass & flukes

Decr 27   1 boat at Crow, 3 draughts caught about 10lbs of cod and flukes

1912 Jany 8th   Overhauled 2 boats when they returned to Appledore from fishing and found in boat one fluke

Jany 10th   1 boat one draught at Crow and 1 at Paige's Pill caught about 12lbs of bass & flukes

I have inquired of several of the Appledore Fishermen about the average weight of coarse fish caught each tide and the reply I received was 'I don't know. I let the old woman have them and she did not say what weight'.

Barnstaple, Thomas Light out on several occasions

Jany 11   2 draughts at the Crow and 2 at Paige's Pill, caught about 12lbs of bass, soles & flukes

Jany 15   Overhauled one, found about 15lbs of bass and flukes

There was only one other boat out from Barnstaple about twice. Thomas Light informed me the average weight caught by him at each tide would be from 45lbs to 50lbs of soles, bass, whiting, plaice, flukes and mullet.

Mr Beara stated that he had interviewed many of the fishermen at Appledore and they said they had had extremely good catches and their being able to fish for coarse fish during some of the winter months was a splendid thing for them.

Mr Draper explained that the Barnstaple fishermen did not receive their nets in time to carry out any fishing.

Having pleased one group of fishermen in the estuary the Conservators met with the complaints of another, as this petition received in December 1913 shows.

Trawler's Petition

The Clerk read the following petition dated 9 December 1913.

'I am desired by the Trawlers of Bideford and Instow to lay before you on their behalf the matter of trawling in the river and to ask your favourable consideration of the matter. The trawlers feel strongly that they are not at all fairly treated and that they should be allowed to trawl in the river. In the first place it can be proved that there has never been any salmon caught in a trawl net, because it is an impossibility, seeing that the net is dragged along the bottom at a very slow rate. The salmon fishermen however say that the trawls would interfere with their drafts, but the trawlers – if permission were granted to them – would be satisfied with a time in season when the salmon fishermen are not using their nets, from 15 September to the last day of December in each year.

As regards doing harm, on the contrary trawling in the river would do much good because thousands of crabs which destroy an enormous amount of small fish would be killed. The draft fishermen are permitted to catch coarse fish at given times, but the trawlers are stopped the whole year round, and as in the winter time it is difficult and very often impossible for the trawlers to get out or venture near the bar, there would be times when a few shillings might be earned by being allowed to trawl in the river; this would not be an every-day occurrence. We would also point out that the trawling proposed is done in an open boat from 15 to 16 feet long and not from the ordinary trawling skiff so that it would always be open and under the watch and supervision of the water bailiffs at all times. If you would permit us we would gladly send a deputation to your Board to discuss the matter with you in all its bearings. Trusting that you will give this your favourable consideration.'

Signed on behalf of the trawlers of Bideford and Instow Charles L. Dark; master & owner of the trawling skiff *Wave* of Bideford.

It was resolved on the motion of Mr Pope and seconded by Mr Pearce *That* the petition be formally acknowledged and that the petitioners be advised to consult the Board of Agriculture and Fisheries and that the Clerk pepare an epitome of what had taken place regarding Trawling by-laws.

Tailpiece: The Bailiff's Motor-cycle

On 18 October 1912 the Board of Conservators for the Taw and Torridge Fishery District meeting at Barnstaple considered the following request:

Application for Motor-cycle

The Clerk read the following application from Supt Gregory for a motor-cycle:

'I beg to make an application to the Board of Conservators for a Motor-cycle. I may state that the advantage of a motor-cycle would be that I could leave my station at any time to work the upper parts of the district; take the Lyn that's twenty miles from Barnstaple before any one can get on any part of it, also the upper part of the Torridge that's about twenty-four miles, and if anyone goes by rail it's known as soon as he leaves any Station that he is about, and I do not consider that it would be much more expense in the long run than it is at the present; my expenses since November 1910 when I was appointed Superintendent Water Bailiff in train fares and night allowances have been £23, and £4 a year cycle allowance. There are some nights I should be glad to stay away but a good many I have had to stay away I should be able to return to my station at Barnstaple.

The image of Superintendent Gregory taking a break-neck bicycle ride from Lynton Station to Barbrook Mill springs to mind. Be this as it may, the Conservators were obviously well aware that their Superintendent Bailiff was working against unreasonable odds, for we may read on:

The Watch Committee recommended that the application be granted.

It was resolved on the motion of Mr Turrall and seconded by Mr Sanders

That Supt Gregory be granted the use of a Motor-cycle and that a committee be appointed to decide upon the make with power to purchase.

It was also resolved on the motion of Mr Norman and seconded by Mr Sanders

That the Committee consist of The Chairman, Mr J.P. Downing and Mr Turrall.

Examination of the records of licensed motor-vehicles in Devon together with those of the Fishery Conservators shows that a 'Premier' motor-cycle was duly registered on 25 November and delivered to Gregory on 28 November 1912. The registration number was T 2643 and the machine weighed 1¾ cwt and rated 3½ h.p. 'G. Boyle' (possibly a man of that name then running a prosperous drapery business at Bideford, acting as agent) was paid £41.18s.7d. for 'Motorcycle etc.' on 13 December. Insurance cost £2.10s. and licence £1.

On 9 March 1915 the number T 2643 was transferred to a 4¼ h.p. B.S.A. weighing 234lbs: the Conservators had traded in the 'Premier' in part exchange. A.S. Jones, cyclemaker of Barnstaple, allowed them £24 for the old machine against the £63 for the B.S.A.

— 7 —

NEWFOUNDLAND
DEVON'S FURTHEST WEST

Historically speaking Devon's furthest west could be said to be not Maker or Werrington (for both were once within the county), but Newfoundland.

Newfoundland lies off the mainland of North America in a position analogous to that of the British Isles in relation to Europe. Significantly, Newfoundland became a Province of Canada only after the referendum of 1948. Factors linked to the history of its fishing industry, and doubtless also linked to the climate of the area, combined to make 2000 miles of the North Atlantic less of a barrier than the 10 miles of Belle Isle Strait.

The English were by no means the first to fish off the Grand Banks, but the first phase of European exploitation is outside the scope of this book. However from the early seventeenth to the early nineteenth century, the South West of England, together with the Channel Islands and parts of Ireland at a somewhat later period, played a leading role in the Newfoundland fishing industry. The involvement of the South West was, indeed, instrumental in creating the type of settlement peculiar to Newfoundland.

Following several early attempts at orthodox colonization, English governments of the late seventeenth and early eighteenth centuries specifically discouraged such measures in order to protect a near monopoly of the cod trade based on English labour and capital. The labour was drawn specifically from the South West, although the capital seems to have been somewhat more broad-based. Hostilities between French and English in the same period further disrupted the pattern of settlement. Thus, while a generally permanent English population remained in certain well-defined areas of the island, it was composed of constantly changing individuals who 'commuted' between Newfoundland and their homeland. Population fluctuated with the seasons and also with the fortunes of war and the variations in the shoals of fish. The majority of the inhabitants were directly employed in catching and curing cod for export to Europe. Only at a comparatively late date did those of European descent but born in Newfoundland form the majority of the population.

Studies of Newfoundland's fishery and population have been international and indeed, intercontinental. Pride of place must be given to the late Dr Matthews of the Memorial University of Newfoundland, whose in-depth studies led him to examine family and individual case histories. Professor H.A. Innis of the
University of Toronto, author of The Cod Fisheries: The history of an International Economy, *has, on the other hand, worked on relationships between New England and Newfoundland in a way which is now being re-examined by workers in the United States.*

The present study, which embodies a most useful general summary, has also been chosen for its local provenance.

Devon and the Cod Fishery of Newfoundland

Up to 1600

When John Cabot, sailing out of Bristol in 1497, discovered Newfoundland and its fishery, England was adequately supplied by its inshore catches and by a flourishing cod industry with Iceland.[1]

Cabot returned to Newfoundland in 1498 and other vessels sailed from Bristol in the following years[2] but they were commercially unsuccessful. Among the first to go from Devon were the *Mary of Guilford* and the *Samson*, which sailed from Plymouth in 1527. The first record in the Plymouth muniments is apparently an entry in 1543–4 of an extra 8d. being paid to the watchman at Rame for lighting beacons 'by night when the Newfoundland men came in'.[3] Indeed, only a handful of English ships made the trip before 1550. After 1550, with expanding royal and merchant navies, more vessels from south-western ports undertook the trip, including some from Plymouth, the Exe estuary, Teignmouth, Bideford and Barnstaple. They totalled no more than fifty in the 1570s, far fewer than their continental rivals.

Devon merchants, with about thirty vessels in the fishery, soon realized that success depended on overseas sales. They opted for the 'dry' or lightly salted, comparatively small, off-shore cod which were considered to be the most palatable and commanded the highest prices. They averaged 10 to 12 pounds and, after being cured on the Newfoundland beaches during the summer months, retained their quality for long periods in hot climates and thus were popular in southern France, Portugal and Spain.[4,5] The lack of domestic salt was

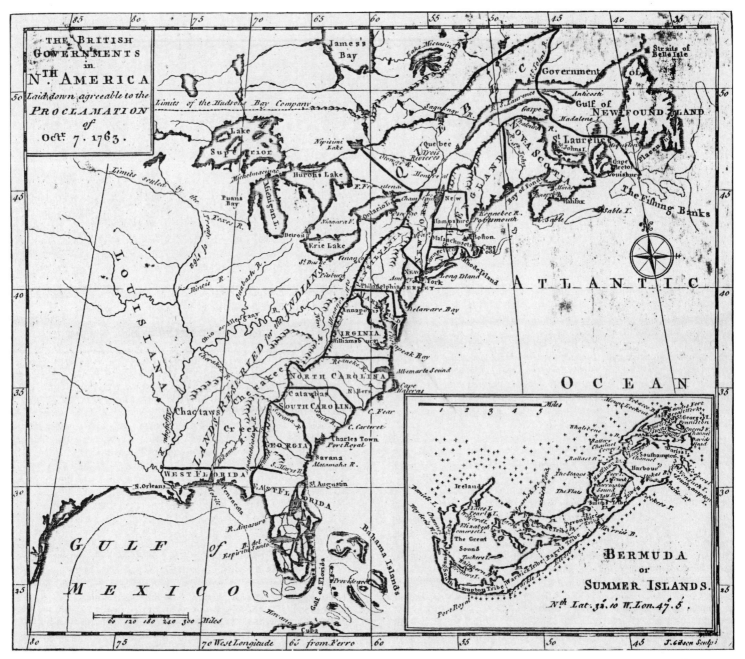

British North America in 1763, following the defeat of the French in Canada. Notice the prominence given to 'The Fishing Banks' off Newfoundland (D.Vaugham Esq.Q.C.)

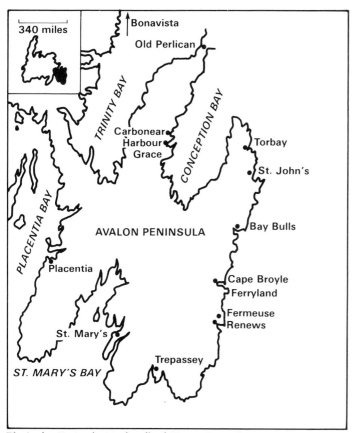

The Avalon Peninsula, Newfoundland (Trans. Devon Assoc.)

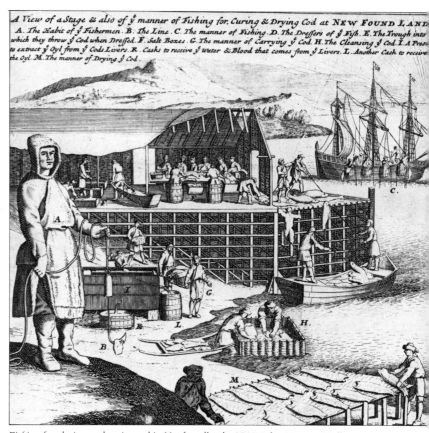

Fishing for, drying and curing cod in Newfoundland c.1717 (after Herman Moll)

a severe disadvantage that had to be overcome. These seemingly simple conclusions involved a complicated organization.

The first requirements were a sheltered harbour and adjacent sands on which the cod could be laid out. On arrival the ships, which averaged 50 to 100 tons, were secured and the cargo off-loaded.[5,6] 'Fishing rooms' were then erected from timber near at hand and comprised a landing stage, rooms for dressing the cod and pressing out the train oil and a beach for salting and drying. Small open fishing boats had also to be built if none remained from the previous year. These preliminaries engaged the crews for up to six weeks and were ordinarily completed by the end of May, in anticipation of the arrival of the capelin, small subarctic fish which rose from the depths to spawn along the shore some time in June or early July. They attracted vast shoals of cod and marked the start of the fishing season proper. When fishing started, the crews divided into groups of six with four fishing and two, sometimes boys in their early teens, dressing the cod under supervision ashore. At the end of the season,

usually in August, the ships returned to their home ports, where the fish and train oil were sold, much of the cod going overseas to Catholic countries.[4,7]

Between 1570 and 1600 the whole structure of the fishery changed to England's advantage. The French faced growing hostility at home between Catholics and Protestants which culminated in open warfare. Spain, just when it had reached its peak with over a hundred sail in the fishery, forcibly annexed Portugal in 1581, lost many of its vessels to English pirates and then suffered the disaster of the Armada. Meanwhile, Holland dominated the North Sea fishery and in 1580 Denmark restricted English access to Icelandic cod. As a result, many fishermen and their families from ports on the east coast joined the expanding Devon fishery and settled permanently.[8] Before the end of the century the West Country sent about a hundred ships each year, half of them from Plymouth.

The Devon fishery relied on free enterprise, in that anyone with the necessary financial backing could man and victual a ship and send it off and on return, share the profit with the crew. Indeed, the sea captains knew that their pay depended upon the size of the catch and their ability to bring it safely home. They were hard men and doubtless most of them wished to avoid trouble but, with several nations competing for trade in a lawless age and often in the shadow of war in Europe, they sometimes provoked or were victims of force or outright piracy. Some kind of solution had to be found to the affrays over fishing rooms, preferably incorporating the custom of choice by order of arrival. Eventually, the 'Admiral' system was introduced whereby the captain of the first ship to enter a bay was responsible for law and order in that bay for the season; it may sometimes have succeeded, especially when the captain with the strongest claim arrived first.

By the end of the century the foundations of the new industry were laid. Some shipowners were beginning to make substantial profits and to commit people living in and near ports to a way of life, whether at sea or ashore, upon which they depended for their living. Shipbuilding thrived and large quantities of foodstuffs and manufactured goods were provided for the expanding merchant navy. In return for the cod, wine and semi-tropical products were imported from the Continent with, whenever possible, Spanish gold and silver and solar salt.

1600–1650

In the sixty years from the early 1580s until the Civil War a remarkable expansion of the Newfoundland fishery took place. At the peak, between 1610 and 1630, Devon had up to 10 000 men at sea, with Plymouth and Dartmouth each supplying more than eighty vessels and 2000 to 3000 men in some years. Barnstaple and Bideford also made notable contributions. Much of the credit for this achievement must go to the West Country shipowners and fishermen without whose tenacity and stoicism it would not have been possible. They had the support of Parliament and the Privy Council, because they were good for trade and valuable as mariners in time of war. They were opposed by would-be colonists and rival shipowners in London and elsewhere. They also had to contend with one of the worst periods of piracy in English history and, as ever, with competition from the French. Yet they managed to retain their objective of catching fish and selling it at a profit, but at the cost of the lives of many of their seamen.

With the end of hostilities in Europe in 1604 and the demise of the Spanish fishery, England and France could anticipate a lucrative trade in Newfoundland provided they confined their fishing to different areas. The French, starting from widely separated ports at home, established themselves in Placentia and the north-western part of the island with outports further north towards the St Lawrence Seaway. The English, with most of their men coming from the West Country and particularly Devon, were a much more compact community and exploited the eastern seaboard with its fine fishing-grounds along the Avalon Peninsula. Men from South Devon fished the northern part from Old Perlican down to Cape Broyle and

including St John's while those from Barnstaple and Bideford favoured the southern shore from Cape Broyle to Trepassey.[9] They were joined by vessels from Dorset, mainly Poole, in Conception and Trinity Bays and a few from Bristol at Harbout Grace. This arrangement had obvious advantages. The selection of 'Admirals' was thereby simplified and they in turn could more easily adjudicate upon the allocation of fishing rooms and arrange for the transfer home for trial of anybody who had committed a serious crime.

The sudden expansion of the fishery called for an early assessment of the economics of a successful trip. This was done in about 1615 for a 100-ton vessel with a crew of forty, which would cost an estimated £420 to fit out.[10,11] Eight crews of three men would each catch about 25 000 cod, giving a total of 200 000 fish (about 100 tons) for sale in continental ports. The additional 12 tons of train oil would probably be brought back to England, much of it being made into soap, and another 10 000 green cod for home consumption. These items might bring a total income of £2250, one-third going to the master and ship's company, the remainder being split between the owner and the victuallers.

A routine for recruitment and the catching and disposing of the fish was devised which continued with fluctuations for the next 200 years. In January and February agents sought crews in villages and towns on or near the coast. They signed on men and boys in taverns and at local fairs and sent them off to help in the preparation of their ships, which had to be self-sufficient in all respects for a voyage of at least four months.[6] When the trade reached its peak in 1635 an estimated 20 000 Englishmen were employed at sea, about half of them from Devon. Some of the vessels became grossly overcrowded so that, despite sleeping in shifts, crewmen often had to doss-down on deck. Occasionally the number of men approximated to the tonnage, a hardship that was not rectified until Letters Patent dated 1665 restricted 'the ratio of sixty persons to 100 tons burthen'. Even so, in 1675 the 80-ton *Crown* carried seventy-eight men from Bideford to Renews.[6]

With insufficient space for the cod on the return journey and the perpetual problem of having an adequate supply of salt – over 7000 tons were needed each year [12] – something more than small ships packed with men and stores was required. Most of the difficulties were overcome by the introduction of 'sac' ships, perhaps deriving their name from the French and Portuguese wine they brought home. They were ordinarily 100 to 200 tons and carried a small crew with much more storage space. They arrived in Newfoundland in late July or early August laden with general stores and departed with cod for the continental markets. In a good year they might make two trips or trade poor quality fish for rum and molasses in the West Indies before collecting more fish for Europe. Thus, sac ships increased the volume of cod that could be carried away without taking any part in the actual fishing and had space for merchandise on the outward trip. Devon merchants, who owned some of the sac ships, disapproved of these developments, which they saw as a threat to their mastery of the dry fishery and a loss of business for their home ports.

From time to time, fishermen remained on the island until the following summer season. They might join one of the colonists or, given adequate provisions, spend the winter tending their employer's fishing rooms and boats on their own. In the 1630s Gabriel Viddomas of Berry Pomeroy was persuaded by a widow, Mrs Weymouth of Carbonear, to stay and work for her a few years before returning home and eventually becoming a ships captain.[8] These early settlers or 'planters', nearly all from Devon, mostly remained for two summers and a winter; a few stayed longer, but nearly all returned to England in due course. By 1630, planters were wintering in most of the thirty or so favourite inlets from Old Perlican to Trepassey and they attracted a new kind of speculator, again mainly from Devon. These were 'bye boat keepers' who went out each summer and reclaimed their open fishing boats which had been maintained during the off season. They engaged their boatmen as best they could, sometimes from the planters but usually by taking them out with them on any fishing or sac ship with available space.

Amid the general confusion of the rapidly expanding industry with colonists, planters, bye boat keepers and London shipowners all fighting for their rights and the numerically much stronger Western Venturers resisting their intrusions, clashes could not be avoided. Thefts were common and sometimes reached serious proportions. For example, part of Sir Walter Raleigh's fleet, returning from Orinoco in 1618, taxed all the fishermen they could find for possessing powder and shot and took away 130 of their men.[13] Far greater hazards existed at sea. Sudden storms and affrays with the French caused some loss of life but the greater danger was piracy in European waters. The Barbary Muslims of North Africa, waiting at the entrance to the English Channel or outside the ports to which the cod was likely to be brought, captured thousands of seamen whom they took home and sold into slavery. The menace was not finally overcome until the 1670s, some years after the boom in the Devon fishery had subsided.

By 1640 West Countrymen controlled the eastern coast from Bonavista to Trepassey with its 500 or so settlers and 1000 servants.[14] Their knowledge of the fishery and corporate loyalty had overcome incursions by the chartered companies and they looked forward confidently to the future. Unfortunately for them, the Civil War of 1642–6 brought trading to a standstill.

1650–1700

In the aftermath of the Civil War, Devon shipowners faced considerable difficulties in their attempts to regain control of the fishery. They were left with the purely fishing aspect, that is, they might send out ships as best they could and sell the bulk of the catch to sac ships in Newfoundland. For this they needed some continuity from year to year, something which was virtually impossible with frequent calls for their men to join the navy and embargoes on fishing during wars and threats of wars. A series of Navigation Acts between 1651 and 1667 were adopted to aid the merchants by relieving them of taxes and insisting that all fish brought to England should be caught and carried in English ships, but the country mustered only about fifty ships in 1652, mainly from Dartmouth and Barnstaple, and made little progress before the end of the Third Dutch War in 1674. This was a considerable blow to the many people who depended directly or indirectly on the trade. Plymouth and Exeter, with little interest in the fishery, were less affected than the other main ports in the county. Dartmouth was sorely tried and in addition suffered two crippling blows from which it took a generation to recover; in 1667 three of its ships and 180 men on board sank when they struck ice off St John's and during the Third Dutch War it lost twenty-seven ships in the two years 1672–4.[15]

When West Country merchants sought their former business in earnest after 1660, they took with them thousands of English and Irish emigrants, the latter coming from Cork and Waterford where outgoing ships, mainly from Bideford and Barnstaple, called for supplies of beef and pork to feed their crews. Most of them had the misfortune to arrive in Newfoundland when cod was scarce. Finding little work, many ran into debt and became unruly until they moved on to New England where they formed the nucleus of the developing winter cod industry. Meanwhile, the merchants resented the planters, some of whom had built substantial fishing establishments on sites previously occupied by them. Yet by 1675 there were only an estimated 204 planters and their 1286 servants and four-fifths of them were of West Country stock,[8] the others being the residue of the former attempts at colonization. The largest settlement was St John's with 185 inhabitants and the smallest Torbay with fourteen, all men.

The interests of the planters and of the Western Venturers remained unresolved, however, until 1671. In that year H.M. Council for Foreign Plantations recommended that permanent colonization in Newfoundland should cease. It was apparently a triumph for men of the west and their motto of 'By West and By Right'. An unsettled decade followed, many planters went to New England, while shipowners in England were adversely affected by the shortage of permanent agents in Newfoundland. The decision was reversed in 1680.

The formal recognition of limited settlement was, hopefully, a signal for the general development of the island. The Avalon Peninsula was firmly in English hands and a new generation of shipowners, better educated than their predecessors, successfully ensured cooperation between the sea captains, the bye boat keepers and the settlers, and acceptance of the authority of the 'Admirals'. Unhappily, the prosperity was not to be sustained. Not only were there few fish to be caught in the 1680s, but Anglo-French relations were becoming strained once more. The French had rapidly expanded their holdings in Placentia from 1662 onwards and, by imposing a duty on fish going into France and securing favourable terms for themselves in Italian markets, they became formidable rivals. After war broke out between the two countries in 1689 the Royal Navy, short of men, stopped the Newfoundland fishing fleet, thereby leaving 3000, or so settlers unprotected for the next four years. The French attacked Ferryland in 1694 and in the following year destroyed all the English settlements except Carbonear Island and Bonavista, sending hundreds of settlers to prison in Placentia and most of the rest back to England. In 1697 the English fleet easily overcame French resistance and the settlers returned to their former lives.

1700–1750

At the beginning of the century Anglo-French discord was still unresolved. The two adversaries, with no longer any serious competition from the Spanish and Portuguese, had the trade to themselves. They were of similar size and each, with governmental support, strove to remain intact despite recurrent wars in Europe but, when the occasion presented, was prepared to inflict damage on the other. At last, in 1713, war with France in Europe came to an end at the Treaty of Utrecht the French ceded the whole island to Britain, whilst retaining fishing rights on the north shore to the west of Bonavista. The fishing grounds at once became safer than they had been for many years.

The period 1700–1730 was distressingly hard for the West Country fishery. Despite the relative peace at sea, good relations with the settlers and European markets taking all the fish they could obtain, cod became scarce particularly after 1715. Few shipowners could make a profit and many were ruined. The home ports, especially Dartmouth, lost much of their main source of income. The situation in Newfoundland was no better, where the population fluctuated violently between 1700 and 4000 with half or more of them leaving after a bad summer, rather than remaining to face possible starvation. Civil disorder, robbery and violence were difficult to control, especially among the unemployed in the winters. A Governor was appointed in 1729 and magistrates were finally accepted in the outports in 1732.

Between 1730 and 1750 the cod returned and the prospects were good. The Western Venturers once more assumed virtually complete control of the English shore. The planters and bye boat keepers thrived and the Southern Spaniards and Italians again enjoyed their 'lightly salted hard cod'. The New England fishery grew apace with increasing demands for cod from the West Indies which, in turn, supplied large quantities of rum to the taverns in St John's. Other American colonies down to Virginia added their merchandise to the general trading. Nova Scotia was developing farm products in addition to its fishery. It was indeed a period in which the various British elements worked harmoniously together, albeit with each jealous of its share of the cod which for the time being were plentiful.[16]

1750–1800

Progress in the renascent fishery was delayed by further Anglo-French disharmony. The outbreak of the Seven Years War in 1756 was followed by attacks on the West Country migratory fleet in home waters and the closure of European markets. In 1761 the French again captured most of the English shore, including St John's, but surrendered to the Royal Navy a few months later. In 1763, a memorable year in the history of the island, peace followed the conquest of Canada and, at the Treaty of Paris, Labrador and the Magdalen Islands were attached to Newfoundland. There followed a dozen years of remarkable prosperity.

The sudden resurgence of trade in 1763 forced West Country shipowners to hasten adjustments they had been making in the previous fifty years. The old self-sufficient fishing ships had gone. Instead, a few merchants owned most of the vessels and largely determined the prosperity of the ports from which they traded. The fishing rooms on the English shore were overcrowded and subject to rental, hence the merchants spread their interest to St Mary's and Placentia Bays in the south and to Fogo and Twillingate beyond Bonavista in the north. The method of fishing changed in that shiploads of bye boat keepers and their crews went out each season, collected their fishing boats and fished on the banks for large cod which they took back to the shore for curing and disposal. The other important difference was the use of the West Country fleet primarily as trading vessels. They took out merchandise of all kinds to St John's, by far the largest centre of commerce, and channeled much of the catch through its fine harbour. By 1763, the following ports were associated:[17]

St John's	–	Dartmouth, Exeter, Teignmouth
Bonavista	–	Teignmouth
Bay Bulls	–	Topsham, Dartmouth
Ferryland	–	Dartmouth
Renews, Fermeuse	–	Dartmouth, Teignmouth

In 1775, quite exceptional figures were attained in the fishery. More English ships were at sea than ever before, they carried about 20 000 men out each summer and quadrupled the catch. Dartmouth alone supplied over a hundred vessels and Teignmouth forty-four. The record number of passengers included Irishmen many of whom elected to stay on the island and soon outnumbered the English in some of the southern outports.

The outbreak of the American War of Independence in 1775 threw the West Country fishery into disarray once more. For several years tension had been mounting between commercial leaders in the colonies and England. Then, when Parliament passed a Bill restricting trade in Massachusetts Bay, the colonists retaliated by banning all trade with Newfoundland. By then the islanders had become almost entirely dependent upon New England for their foodstuffs and they faced starvation until supplies eventually arrived from England. The West Country maintained its fleet, reduced in numbers to about one-third by the press-gangs, but faced increasing opposition as first France and then Spain declared war on Britain. All the European markets were closed except Portugal, which almost alone kept the fishery going. The fishing ships, many of them unarmed and not able to find suitable convoys, were attacked on both sides of the Atlantic and an estimated 80 per cent of them were captured or destroyed sooner or later.[18] Many thousands of West

Countrymen of the Royal or Merchant Navies found their way into American, French and Spanish prisons.

With the end of the war in 1783, the Western Venturers were able to resume their trade in the fishery, albeit in rather different circumstances. The Americans, who before the war sent 175 ships to Newfoundland annually,[19] were excluded from there by the Imperial Trades System and also from the West Indies. Newfoundland thus acquired most of the West Indies trade and soon obtained almost all its foodstuffs from Canada and Prince Edward Island. The English government abandoned its policy of limited settlement and during the boom years from 1783 to 1790 saw the resident population rise to 30 000. Devon shipowners were encouraged to consolidate their businesses on the island, where there were by then flourishing fisheries at St John's, Harbour Grace, Carbonear, Ferryland and Placentia. They sent about 150 vessels each year to these various ports and extended their operations to Labrador for salmon and seal.

The Napoleonic Wars lasted almost continuously from 1793 to 1815 and were the final blow for the West Country fishery. The demands of the Royal Navy reduced their crews from thousands to hundreds or even scores; Newman and Co., the well known Dartmouth firm, employed as many foreigners as Englishmen, because of the shortage of the latter.[20] The ships were always at risk in European waters and, with Portugal virtually the only open market for cod, the most hazardous journeys were between there and England. In 1798, twenty-three ships were lost to France and Spain as they tried to enter the harbour of Oporto. In Newfoundland the planters assumed control of the fishery, but even they caught more fish than they could sell. Once more they suffered severely from shortage of food and were denied the option of moving on to New England

1800 and After

By 1800 the population had dropped to about 20 000 through lack of trade. Many found it difficult to survive in the smaller outports and moved to St John's and Trinity and Fortune Bay, but even there work was scarce and irregular. Napoleon's disastrous invasion of Russia and Wellington's victories in Spain opened the markets in Southern Europe and caused the boom years 1811–15. Thousands of migrants, some from the West Country but more from Ireland, arrived to swell the population to 40 000. When peace eventually came in 1815, the boom ended and was followed by years of depression and overpopulation.

At the beginning of the new century, the West Country still had seventy ships out on the Banks, most of them based on Fortune Bay to the west of Placentia Bay but by then control of the fishery had, quite rightly, been taken over by the islanders. The fleet diminished to thirty by 1815, fifteen by 1823 and disappeared by 1844.[20] A few ships continued to go out from Devon throughout the century, mainly to Labrador for cod, salmon and seal, and they left behind a smattering of new settlers.

Alongside the dwindling fishing fleet, Devon merchants continued to be strongly represented and were joined, mainly in the first half of the century, by the colourful 'topsail schooners'. Sailing out of Kingsbridge, Salcombe and Brixham and relying on their speed, they rushed from Northern Newfoundland and Labrador to Mediterranean ports. The merchants transported fish and maintained their business connections with the outports for as long as it was profitable. Newmans did not withdraw from the South Coast until the 1890s, but long before then Devon had yielded to London and Liverpool. The introduction of steamships in the middle of the century transformed the collection and distribution of the cod, which were concentrated in a few towns such as St John's and Harbour Grace. The Devon sailing ships were needed no more.

Devon's Furthest West

Residual links between Newfoundland and the West Country may still be found in unexpected places. In Newfoundland itself, at least until recently, agnatic crew structure and payment by shares in profits betrayed the West Country origin of the organization of fishing in certain well-defined areas. In Devon, there are occasional geographical clues – Newfoundland Cove lies at the mouth of the Dart, Newton Abbot has a (most unworthy) Newfoundland Way marking the site of the Newfoundland Inn, demolished in the mid 1960s. This hostelry is traceable back to 1823 at least, when, most significantly, it was the Newfoundland Fishery Inn.

Scattered over a wider period of time and from a wide variety of sources, documents held by the Devon Record Office attest to an involvement in the Newfoundland trade so wide that even those whom it would be tempting to think of as landsmen were drawn into it.

The earliest references come from the Plymouth Records from such sources as the Old Audit Book and Serjeant Hele's Precedent Book and begin as early as 1543. Plymouth's early involvement with fishing voyages to Newfoundland and New England gave rise to a community which had already accumulated experience in sailing to the West when the *Mayflower* called there in 1620.

Possibly the most historic document held is the record, dated 19 February 1634, of the fees and bribes paid to officials of Charles I's Chancery in obtaining the Western Charter.[21] A total of £101.17s. was divided between Barnstaple (a quarter), Plymouth (three-eighths) and Dartmouth (three-eighths), a circumstance which indicates the partners and their relative importance.

Of similar date is the lawsuit in which Thomas Robins of Stokeinteignhead resisted the claim of the parson of that parish to tithes of fish caught in Newfoundland.[22] This small village was heavily involved in the Newfoundland fishery and the incumbent doubtless wished to capitalize on the new wealth coming into the community.

Hand-in-hand with riches went risks. French and Dutch privateers and pirates, together with those of Islamic North Africa preyed on the Newfoundland traders as cod do on capelin.

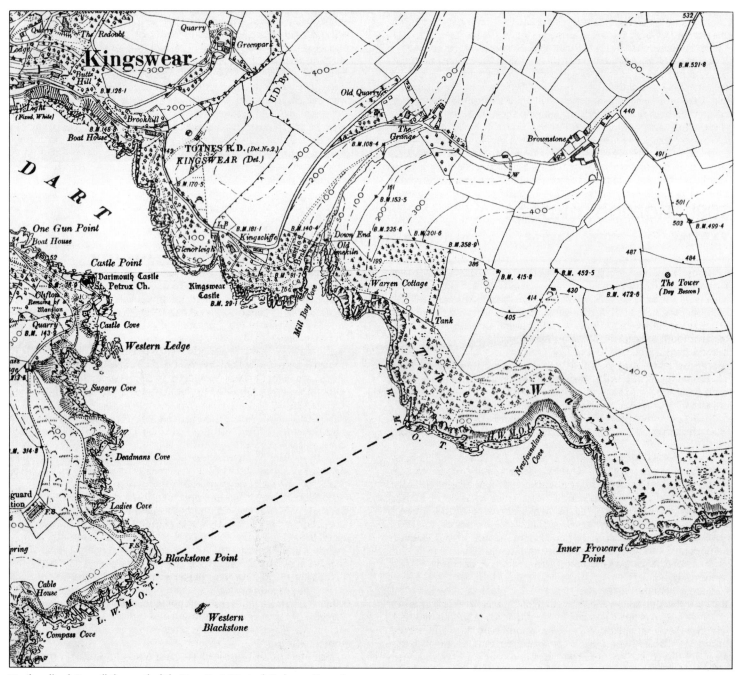

Newfoundland Cove off the mouth of the River Dart (Six-inch Ordnance Survey)

On 4 May 1665, for example, the *Joseph* of Topsham (50 tons), master John Bawden junior, was intercepted by the *Hunter* of Flushing 'a Dutch caper or man of warre' under Captain Jacobson, thirty leagues (*c*.100 miles) west of Scilly, escorted to the 'Groyne' and made a prize of war.[23]

Quite a respectable catalogue of Devon ships and men taken by the Barbary Corsairs can be compiled from existing sources. To maximize the number of prisoners taken they appear to have sunk their prizes and to have taken crews from half-a-dozen or more luckless ships in one voyage. This we know from a remarkable book by Joseph Pitts of Exeter, whose *Faithful Account of the Mahometans* was published in London in 1731,[24] though relating to events of his youth. He was captured in the ship *Speedwell* of Lympstone, bound from Newfoundland to Bilbao on his first long voyage. Independent evidence for the events exists in the petition of Margaret Taylor, for the ransom of her husband, captured on 11 September 1679 in the *Speedwell*, being the ship's master named in Pitts' account.[25] Pitts remained fifteen years in captivity, from a boy of fifteen to a man of thirty years, before escaping.

Henry Hines of Plymouth, also in the Newfoundland trade, had been in captivity for seven years, when 'an Algerine, a very reputable merchant' on business in that port offered to secure his ransom for £40, in 1680.[26]

Armed resistance was by no means general, although the *Blessing* of Dartmouth fought off her assailants, from Sallee in Morocco, for several hours on 2 September 1685. A petition of the relatives of fourteen crew members who survived reached the County justices at Exeter on 12 January 1686. Fifty shillings was awarded in respect of each man.[27]

Having escaped such fates, or indeed even before sailing, all may not have gone smoothly: lawsuits in the Exeter Admiralty Court, for example, record disputes over fitting out before a voyage and over non-payment of wages after. Two of the owners of the *Bilbao Merchant* of Topsham, John Parre and George Tremlett, were sued for not contributing to the cost of a Newfoundland voyage in April 1677.[28]

The case of the wages of the crew of the *Pellican* of Topsham includes particulars of an actual sojourn in Newfoundland. Arriving there on 12 May 1679, the *Pellican* began loading fish on 14 August and was riding at anchor in Bay Bulls with 1650 quintals of dry merchantable Newfoundland fish on 17 September of that year, about which time she sailed for Malaga.[29]

The impact of the return of the Newfoundland men to their homes at the end of the season is vividly evoked by a petition to the Bishop of Exeter in the autumn of 1714.[30] Relating that the population of Brixham was growing too large for its church, it continues 'especially at the Fall of the years when our Newfoundland men return from Sea: that thro' thronging and pressing for Room in it many Differences have risen; that others take occasion hence not to come thither at all . . .'. (It was proposed to meet the problem by building a gallery.)

Other glimpses are more mundane or more domestic. Thomas Hawkins of St John's, Newfoundland, 'planter' (i.e. settler), was presumably able to cut off Mary Wooton of Dartmouth, his mother-in-law, with a shilling in his will without fear of nagging. Ironically, Hawkins' will, dated 10 June, 1724[31], notes that the stamped paper necessary to make a will legal was not obtainable in Newfoundland!

On 25 January 1749, mariner Thomas Kingman of Lympstone and merchant Philip Neyle of Exeter sold a fishing room and three storehouses at 'Fermouse' to mariner Elias Pitt of Teignmouth for £10.10s.[32] The transaction seems to have taken place in Exeter, and deeds exchanged for all the world as if the storehouses lay by the Exe estuary instead of 2000 miles away across the Atlantic.

Similarly the justices assembled in Quarter Sessions at Exeter made arrangements for the sale of the goods of Richard Ball of West Teignmouth, apothecary, a bankrupt in 1755.[33] These included debts to be gathered from customers in Fermeuse, Ferryland, Renews, St Mary's and Trepassey in Newfoundland and from Ideford and Bovey Tracey in Devon.

A broadside ballad of the late eighteenth century[34] entitled 'The Newfoundland Seaman' tells how the deceitful male meets a pretty maid and takes her by the hand, asking her to go with him across the ocean. On her refusal he deludes her with promises that he will return, which are, of course, not honoured when their child is born. A real-life counterpart, George Waneman, was in 1711 'unable to return home. He has Married a second Wife in Spain and has One a Live at Topsham'.

Even to the well-intentioned, the necessity to earn a living in Newfoundland imposed something of a double standard of morality. A letter written in 1675 on behalf of an honest seaman of Alwington (a parish on the North Devon coast) begs that proceedings against him in the Bishop's court for immoral conduct may be stopped. It further explains that the seaman and his now wife were 'acquainted' about Lady day 1674, but that he then had to depart with his ship for Newfoundland. Duly returning, he married his young woman at Bulkworthy. A child was born thirteen weeks later and was properly baptized after which time 'the seaman is again in Newfoundland'.[35]

Two somewhat more moral stories can be found to cap these tales. George Hire of Plymouth was married to Unity Teague by James Brooks, J.P. at Bay Bulls, Newfoundland on 8 October 1772, but, interestingly, he and his bride did not settle there. They were remarried in England 'to prevent any disputes which may arise' as a result of the English Marriage Acts. The ceremony was performed at Yealmpton on 29 December 1785.[36]

Also dating from 1772 is the story of Robert Perriton of West Alvington, found guilty of deserting his family. He was summarily instructed to ship himself in 'some vessel employed in the Newfoundland trade from this day until the following season', from which gainful employment he was to have his master forward 1s.6d. a week for the upkeep of his family, for whom his brother was meanwhile made responsible.[37]

Examined in later life in 1781 after he had settled down at Bovey Tracey, his birthplace, John Samson revealed his story of his youth.[38] Following the death of two masters to whom he was successively

Voyages, my Fancy was to range further abroad; for which I sufficiently suffer'd, as in the sequel of the *Story* will appear.

I shipp'd my self on *Easter Tuesday, Anno* 1678. with one Mr. *George Taylor*, Master of the *Speedwell*, of *Lymson*, near *Exeter* (Mr. Alderman *George Tuthill*, of *Exon*, Owner) bound to the *Western Islands*, from thence to *Newfoundland*, from thence to *Bilboa*, from thence to the *Canaries*, and so home, had God permitted. We got safe to *Newfoundland*; and our Business being ended there, with a fair Wind we set sail for *Bilboa*; and after we had been out about 40 Days from *Newfoundland*, coming near the Coast of *Spain* (which we knew was the Place where the *Algerines* us'd to haunt for poor Ships that come from the *Westward*) we look'd out sharp for Ships, avoiding all we saw; but especially did we look out in the Morning, at Sun-rising, and in the Evening, at Sun-setting. The Day in which we were taken, our *Mate*, Mr. *John Milton*, was early at Top-mast-head, and cried out, *A Sail!* The *Master* ask'd him, *Where?* *At Leeward*, replied the *Mate*, *about five or six Leagues*. And so, to be brief in my *Relation*, About Mid-day, being almost overtaken by them (the Enemy being but about a Mile distance from us) our *Master* said, it will be in vain for us to make our Flight any longer, seeing it will be

be but an Hour or two e'er we shall be taken, and then, probably, fare the worse if we continue our flight. I may leave any Person to judge what an heartless Condition we were in; but yet still we could not forbear kenning the Ship, that unwelcome Object, which, *Devil like*, was eager in the Pursuit of us. All hope now failing, there being no place for Refuge, we haled up our Sails, and waited for them. As soon as the *Pirate* came up with us, the *Captain* being a *Dutch Renegado*, and able to speak *English*, bid us hoist out our Boat; which we could not do without much Trouble and Time, by reason that a few Days before, one of our Men in a great Storm was wash'd overboard, and I my self was so scalded with boiling Water, as to be disabled for working; so that we had but four Men that were able: And therefore, before we could make half ready to hoist out our Boat, they came a-board us in their own. I being but *young*, the Enemy seem'd to me as monstrous ravenous Creatures; which made me cry out, *O, Master! I am afraid they will kill us and eat us. No, no, Child*, said my Master, *they will carry us to* Algier, *and sell us.*

The very first Words they spake, and the first Thing they did, was beating us with Ropes, saying, *Into Boat you* English *Dogs!* And without the least Opposition, with Fear, we tumbled into their Boat, we scarce knew

B 2   how

Joseph Pitts of Exeter vividly recalled in later life the circumstances of his capture by pirates in his 'Faithful Account of the Mahometans' (West Country Studies Library)

apprenticed, he bound himself, aged approximately twenty-four, to John Newman and Company at Dartmouth, the notable Newfoundland merchants. Following a summer in Newfoundland and a winter in England with the company, he set out again across the Atlantic. This time his ship was captured and he became a prisoner of war. Following the usage of the times however, he was after an uncertain period exchanged and was brought back to England with a shipload of fellow prisoners.

Another case, also from Bovey Tracey, concerned Samuel Smale. His master being unable to keep him, he was assigned to agents of Philip Beenlen and Humphrey Cole of St John's Newfoundland on 1 May 1815.[39]

This was indeed the day of the merchants; John Duniam of East Teignmouth, 'Newfoundland Merchant', is recorded with other less spectacular tradesmen in the East Teignmouth registers in 1813.[40]

Devon has thus provided men and ships, but evidence of financial backing at what appears to be 'grass roots' level comes from Surrey, where a record of debts from Newfoundland fishermen (all Devonians or Cornish) has come to light. Investors in the Home Counties appear to have advanced sums on bond to enable individuals to undertake the Newfoundland voyage. The largest sum involved was £104; more typical are sums of £10, £20 or £30. Even so, varying fates overtook those who borrowed such sums. John Symonds of Harberton sold his smallholding before going to Newfoundland, where he died penniless in about 1720; John Hull of Sidmouth was in the Debtor's prison in St Thomas, Exeter in 1730.[41]

Finally we have a glimpse of a ship and her crew setting out from North Devon in 1739.[42] It is provided by a contract dated at Appledore on 3 March in that year for a fishing voyage to Placentia and the Cape. The initial destination – Placentia – is interesting as it was formerly the French base of operations. The master was to have total discretion as to the period for fishing, choice of market and acceptance of cargo home to England. More surprisingly, the crew are expressly excluded from shares in either fish or train oil – a reversal of the earlier state of affairs.

Christopher Chappell, master, and James Chappell and 'company' owners of the ship *Prosperous*, agreed for monetary remuneration with sixteen mariners whose rates of pay are meticulously set out. The master himself was to have £3.10s. per month, and eleven others between £2.10s. (for John Thorn, the mate) and £1. 4s. per month (for Richard Foard, perhaps the least experienced man). Five other men were to receive a fixed standing wage – a mere pittance – for the entire voyage.

Overleaf, page 78:
Pitts' account is confirmed by this petition on behalf of George Taylor, master of the Speedwell *of Lympstone captured on 11 September 1679 (Devon Record Office)*
Overleaf, page 79
George Hire and Unity Teague were married in Newfoundland in 1772 and again in England in 1785 (Yealmpton Parish Records at the West Devon Record Office)

We the Minister, Churchwarden, & other
Inhabitants of the Parish of Lympston, in
the County of Devon, do humbly Certify
this Hon:ble Bench, that Georg Taylour of ye
Parish, Mariner, was taken Captive by an
Algerine man of War, on the Eleventh day of
September, in the Year of oLd, One Thousand
Six Hundred seventy & Nine, And carryed into
Argier, where he still remaineth in Captivity;
And that his Ransom amounteth to One Hundred
& Twenty Pounds Sterling, as appears to us by
Letters received from him And we do farther
humbly Certify, that neither his Wife, nor any
friend of his, is able to disburse so great a
Sum toward his Redemtion. In witness where
of We have hereunto set oLd Hands, this Tenth
day of July, An: Dm: 1682.

(The Year. 1785)   Page 53

No 216

George Hire _____ . of [this] Parish Lieutenant in ye Navy

and Unity Hire — otherwise Teage of [this]

Parish _____ were

Married in this [Church] by [Licence] .

this twenty-ninth Day of December _____ in the Year One Thousand seven Hundred

and eighty five _____ by me John Brooking Luscombe [Curate]

This Marriage was { George Hire

solemnized between Us { The mark of ✕ Unity Hire otherwise Teage

In the { William Anthony

Presence of { Thos. Holberton

217

This is to certify that I James Brooks one of his Majesty's
Justices of the Peace for the District of Bay Bulls in
Newfound Land have this Day joined together in Matrimony
according to the Ceremony of the Church of England
Mr Geo. Hire of Plymouth in the County of Devon
Mariner, and Miss Unity Teage of Bay Bulls in the
District aforesaid. — Given under my hand in Bay Bulls
the th of October 1772 James Bookes J. P.

John Henry Dunn Surgeon } of his Majesty's Ship } Witnesses
Thos Dawkins Purser. { the Nautilus.

The above is a true Copy of a Certificate of Marriage now
in the Possession of Mr George Hire. — But to prevent any
disputes that may arise after his Death has consented to
have the Ceremony again performed in this Church the
Day & year above written.

Thos Holberton }
Willm Anthony }   J B Luscombe Curate of Yealmpton

NOTES AND REFERENCES

Chapter 1

1. Welch, C.E. *Pilchards and Plymouth's Fort* (Fishing Feast Programme 1st July 1961).
2. Gill, C. *A New History of Plymouth – Ice Age to the Elizabethans* (Newton Abbot 1966).
3. Rowse, A.L. The Dispute Concerning the Plymouth Pilchard Fishery, 1584-91 (*Economic History*, January 1932).
4. West Devon Record Office – Worth 359/47.
5. West Devon Record Office – Worth 359/50.
6. Southward, A.J. and Roberts, E.K., The Marine Biological Association 1884–1984 (*Trans. Devonshire Assoc.* Vol. 116 for 1984).
7. Lysons, D. & S., Devonshire (*Magna Britannia* series 1822, Vol. II, p.399).
8. St Andrew's parish church – Bishop's Transcripts for 1830.
9. West Country Studies Library microfilm copies.
10. West Devon Record Office – Plymouth Shipping Registers 12.

Chapter 2

1. Firestone, Melvin M. Crab fishermen in South Devon, (*Devon Historian* 12 (1976) p.3.)
2. Firestone, Melvin M. The crew structure of the Start Bay Crab Fishery, *Anthropological Studies in Great Britain and Ireland* (Anthropological Research Papers No. 27 Arizona State University, Tempe, 1982); and Anderson 'Raoul and Cato' Wadel eds Comparative problems in fishing orientations *North Atlantic Fishermen: anthropological essays in modern fishing* (St John's; Institute of Social Economic Research, Memorial University of Newfoundland, Social and Economic Papers No. 5, 1972) p. 147-150.
3. Fitzgibbon, Theodora, *A taste of the West Country in food and pictures* (London 1975) p. 47.

4. Report of the Commissioners Appointed to Inquire into the Sea Fisheries of the United Kingdom, 1866: Volume II Parliamentary Papers (3596-I) XVIII p. 390.
5. *Ibid.* p. 391
6. Thornton, Patricia A. The demographic and mercantile bases of initial permanent settlement in the Strait of Belle Isle, *Peopling of Newfoundland: essays in historical geography* St John's: Institute of Social and Economic Research, Memorial University of Newfoundland, Social and Economic Papers, No. 8, 1977.
7. Page, John Lloyd Werden, *The coasts of Devon and Lundy Island: their towns, villages, scenery, antiques and legends* (London 1895) p. 327-328.
8. Report of the Commissioners . . . Vol. II. p. 196.
9. Report of the Commissioners . . . Vol. I. Parliamentary Papers (3596) vol XVII Appendix 5.
10. Firestone, Melvin M. *Brothers and rivals; patrilocality in Savage Cove*, St Johns: Institute of Social and Economic Research, Memorial University of Newfoundland, Social and Economic Studies No. 5, 1967, p. 92.
11. Clark, Roy. *The Longshoremen*, Newton Abbot, 1974 p. 52; Report of the Commissioners . . . Vol. II p. 390.
12. Report of the Commissioners . . . Vol. II pp. 196 and 390.
13. Young, Lambton J.H. *Sea-fishing as a sport* (London 1865) p. 76.
14. Clark, Roy, *op. cit.* pp. 137 and 157.
15. Devon Record Office. Tithe Map of Stokenham, 1847. p. 16. 'Higher Grove Field. Apportionment No. 873. Willows, 1 acre, 1 rood, 10 perches. Rent 3/10. Owner: Arthur Holdsworth. Tenant: Philip Loye, Jnr.'
16. D.R.O. Tithe Map of Stokenham – 21 willow groves. These include the groves used by Beesands and Hallsands fishermen. Willows are still growing on the west side of the stream running down the valley to Lannacombe Beach, about a quarter of a mile up (802

375), but they have not been cut for some years and are small trees now. Tithe Map of Chivelstone – 5 willow groves. Three of these were adjoining and ran down a stream nor' nor' east of East Prawle (782 366). The willows were last cut in 1968 and were used for pots. A modern house has been built on the site, still known as Willow Grove. Tithe Map of South Pool – 6 willow groves. Tithe Map of East Portlemouth – 1 willow grove.
17. Wright, Dorothy, *Baskets & Basketry* (Reprint by David & Charles, 1972.) p. 3, fig 46.
18. *Ibid*, p 36, fig. 38.
19. *Ibid*, p 39, fig. 47.

Chapter 3

1. Horsley, J.H. Exeter Papers in Economic History No 1.
2. This passage was written by Walter Garstang, a naturalist with the Marine Biological Assocation, based at the time of publication, in 1903, at Lowestoft, but formerly at Plymouth.
3. Straight Michael, *Report on the Brixham Fishing Industry*, 1935.

Chapter 4

1. The Greenland Right Whale, *Balaena mysticetus*, is non-migratory and grows to a length of 58 feet.
2. Notably in his tract A *View of the Greenland Trade and Whale Fishery with the National and Private Advantages thereof.*
3. For example: cloth and leather to Spain, fish and timber from Newfoundland.
4. The Exe entrance was encumbered with shoals and carried barely six feet of water at Low Water Springs. Large vessels could not use the ship canal at this time, and loading and unloading was at drying quays or from lighters.
5. The Exeter Whale Fishery Ledger (Devon Record Office).
6. Six attended in the best year of trading; almost thirty in the worst.
7. Clark, E.A.G., *The Ports of the Exe Estuary 1660–1860.*
8. She was advertised for sale in the *Exeter Flying Post*, 1 March 1783.
9. Herman Katenkamp, a merchant who invested £125.
10. The South Seas Company fleet of 1730 had averaged one whale per ship per season.
11. Keble Chatterton, E., *Whalers and Whaling.*
12. It was finally discontinued in 1824.
13. Henry Elking gives as forty-three the crew of a 300–ton whaler, and Frank Smyth forty as the crew of a 350–ton vessel of the period. Frank Bullen and Dr Felix Maynard both give thirty-seven as the crew total for nineteenth-century whalers.
14. Chief harpooner. Dutch term, and also spelt 'specksioneer' and 'specksynder'.
15. Topsham had a reputation for alert seamen who were supposed to sleep with their doors open so as to be ready for any emergency. The local expression, ' . . . where do 'ee come from? Topsham?' addressed to someone who has left a door open is still current.
16. The Ledger of Matthew Lee (Devon Record Office).

17. Figures taken from Appendix 29 of the Third Report on the State of British Fisheries, Vol. 10 of *Reports of Committees of the House of Commons, 1785–1801*. (See Table 5, p40.)
18. Notably the Japan Grounds, which were pioneered by the British whaler *Syren* in 1819.
19. Somers Cocks, J.V., *Devon Topographical Prints 1660–1870* (Exeter 1977, No. 2702) (a copy is in the Devon & Exeter Institution); Ellis, H.S., Oyster Breeding of the French System (T.D.A., i, iv, 1865, pp. 95–6); Horsley, John, 'South Devon Fisheries' (*Torquay Natural History Society Transactions*, XVI, i, 1970–71, pp. 17–23).
20. Bulleid, P.S., 'The Yealm Oyster Fishery' (T.D.A., LXXI, 1939, pp. 188–9); Trump, H.J., *Westcountry Harbour* (Teignmouth 1976, p.122).
21. DRO, 1039 M/L 24. (OS SX 97 W.).
22. *Western Times*, (15 December 1885; 4 February 1887).
23. *Devon Weekly Times*, (20 March 1885); *Western Times*, (17 March 1885).
24. *Western Times*, (20 March 1885).
25. *Western Times*, (1 December 1885).
26. Malicious Injuries to property Act 24 & 25 Vict c97 1861.
27. What follows is from *Western Times* (1 February 1887); *Devon Weekly Times* (4 February 1887).
28. Leases to this effect are in DRO 1309 M/L 21–33.

Chapter 5

1. DRO 96M/Box 2/9.
2. Reynolds, Stephen, *A Poor Man's House*, London Magazine Editions, 1980, pp175-6.
3. DRO 96M/Box 33/9C.
4. DRO 96M/Box 2/1.
5. DRO Moger CC4/111.
6. The fishermen's line is very different from the tackle makers' arrangements. It varies a little locally. At Seacombe, the upper part consists of 2–3 fathoms of stoutish conger line, to take the friction over the gunwale, and 5–6 fathoms of finer line, to the end of which a conical 'sugarloaf' lead is attached by a clove hitch, the short end being laid up around the standing part for an inch or so and then finished off with the strong, neat difficue [corruption of difficult?] knot. A swivel, or better still simply an eyelet cut from an old boot, runs free, just above the lead, between the clove hitch and difficue knot. To the eyelet is attached the 'sid' – i.e. two or three fathoms of fine snooding; – to the sid a length of gut on which half an inch of clay pipe-stem is threaded, and to the gut a rather large hook. The bait is a 'lask', or long three-cornered strip of skin, cut from the tail of a mackerel. The older fishermen prefer a round lead, cast in the egg-shell of a gull, because it runs sweeter through the water, but with this form the fish's bite is difficult to feel on account of the jerk having to be transmitted through the heavy bulky piece of lead.

The lines are trailed astern of the boat as it sails up and down, where the mackerel are believed to be. When well on the feed they will bite, even at the pipe clay and bare hook, faster than can be hauled inboard. River anglers and even some sea fishers are disposed to deny the amount of skill, alertness and knowledge which go to catching the greatest possible number of fish while they are up. It is often said that the mackerel allows itself to be caught as easily by a beginner as by an old hand. One or two mackerel may: mackerel don't. In hooking, as opposed to fishing fine with a rod, the sporting element is supplied by fish, not *a* fish; by numbers in a given time, not bend and break. The tackle brought to the sea by the superior angler, who thinks he knows more than those who have hooked mackerel for generations, is a wonder, delight, and irritation to professional fishermen: it is constructed in such robust ignorance of the habits, and manner of biting, of mackerel, and it ignores so obstinately the conditions of the sport. Likewise the fish ignore *it*.

Chapter 6
1. Clovelly PR2.
2. Moger CC 3/20
3. Moger CC 3/6.
4. Chanter, J.F., 1907 *History of Lynton and Countisbury*, (Exeter) p.26.
5. From Lord Clinton's papers. Translated from the original deed by H.A. Hewlett, Gray's Inn, 1866.
6. From the Earl of Halsbury's papers. Transcribed from *Star Chamber Proceedings*, Bundle 27, 388.
7. *Ibid.*, Bundle 23, 166.
8. From Lord Clinton's papers. Transcribed from depositions filed in Chancery, Mitford Pt. 6, No. 637.
9. From Lord Clinton's papers
10. Prince, *Worthies of Devon*, 2nd Ed., p.52.
11. From Lord Clinton's papers.
12. *Ibid.*
13. *Ibid.*
14. *Ibid.*
15. *Gentleman's Magazine*, 67, ii.
16. From Lord Clinton's papers.
17. *Teste* W.F. Dean, formerly employed by the Clinton Estate.
18. DRO Fishery Board 5/1 is the source for this and the following extracts in this section.
19. DRO 2131 O/X/LR 12-13.

(The author expressed his debt to Lord Clinton and to the Earl of Halsbury for permission to use papers then in their possession.)

Chapter 7
1. Biggar, H.P., 1911 *Precursors of Jacques Cartier 1498–1534*. (Ottawa p.20.)
2. Judah, C.B., 1933. *The North American Fisheries and British Policy to 1713*. (Urbana, p.13.)
3. Beckerlegge, J.J., 1936–7, Plymouth Muniments and Newfoundland. (*Trans. Plymouth Inst.*, 18, 3–23.)
4. Innis, H.A., 1954. *The Cod Fisheries. The History of an International Economy*. (Toronto, pp. 50–51.)
5. Russell, P., 1950. *Dartmouth*. (Callington, p.64.)
6. Matthews, K., 1973. *Lectures on the History of Newfoundland*. (Newfoundland, pp. 78–79.)
7. Innis, H.A., 1954. *op. cit.* pp. 31–32.
8. Russell, P., 1950. *op. cit.* pp. 71 and 82.
9. Matthews, K., 1973. *op. cit.* p. 231.
10. Innis, H.A., 1954. *op. cit.* pp. 57–59.
11. Russell, P. 1950. *op. cit.* p. 83.
12. Innis, H.A., 1954. *op. cit.* p. 60.
13. *Ibid.* pp. 62–64.
14. *Ibid.* pp. 67–70.
15. Russell, P., 1950. *op. cit.* 124.
16. *Ibid.* pp. 144–160.
17. *Ibid.* p. 146.
18. Matthews, K., 1973. *op. cit.* p. 42.
19. *Ibid.* p. 58.
20. *Ibid.* pp. 211–215.
21. 175 M/O 1.
22. Moger CC 5/317.
23. Moger CC 181/18/3.
24. Westcountry Studies Library, Exeter.
25. Devon Q/S 128/77/6.
26. Devon Q/S 128/99/6.
27. Devon Q/S 128/42/26.
28. Chanter 780 d.
29. Chanter 780 d.
30. Faculty Causes: Brixham 1.
31. Moger CC 211/53.
32. 924 B/T 41.
33. 924 B/B 8/12.
34. 997 Z/Z 9.
35. Moger 'Basket A' 2749.
36. West Devon Record Office, Plymouth P 731/.
37. West Alvington PO 135.
38. Bovey Tracey PO 710, 736, 780.
39. Bovey Tracey PO 666.
40. East Teignmouth PR 3.
41. Surrey Record Office, Kingston-on-Thames, Elwill papers.
42. 2422 M/B 1.

INDEX

All entries in italics indicate illustrations